Cat Tales

A Guideposts Book

Guideposts®

CARMEL, NEW YORK 10512

www.guidepostsbooks.com

Every attempt has been made to credit the sources of copyrighted material used in this book. If any such acknowledgment has been inadvertently omitted or miscredited, receipt of such information would be apprediated.

ACKNOWLEDGMENTS

For all material that originally appeared in *Angels on Earth*, it is reprinted with permission. Copyright © 1997, 1998 by Guideposts, Carmel, NY 10512

For all material that originally appeared in *Daily Guideposts*, it is reprinted with permission. Copyright © 1982, 1984, 1990, 1992, 1993, 1994, 1997 by Guideposts, Carmel, NY 10512

For all material that originally appeared in *Guideposts* magazine, it is reprinted with permission. Copyright © 1975, 1983, 1994, 1995, 1997, 1998 by Guideposts, Carmel, NY 10512

The interior cat illustrations originally appeared in *Cats and Kittens Iron-On Transfer Patterns* by Janette Aiello. Copyright © 1983 by Janette Aiello. Reprinted with permission from the publisher Dover Publications, Inc.

www.guideposts.org
Cover design by Viqui Maggio
Interior design by José R. Fonfrias
Composition by Composition Technologies, Inc.
Printed in the United States of America

Table of Contents

PART THREE • FRIENDS

Introduction

We cannot help but marvel at the variety and uniqueness of God's creation: giraffes, elephants, horses, alligators! Each has a place in our world, living in a chain of life that is awe-inspiring. And then there is that little animal, the domesticated cat, who seems to be human at times—living with us, communicating, teaching and loving. They worm their way into our hearts, enriching our lives and teaching us lessons about relationships that we would be reluctant to learn from a human companion, as our egos get in the way.

In the everyday busy-ness of life, we sometimes take these feline companions for granted. Unless they are ill, lost or scratching our favorite chair, we might just enjoy their warm purring motor next to us as we sleep. But what a marvel they are—God's creatures who seem uniquely to complement our human lives.

Here are stories of cats as teachers, angels and friends: some of those moments when a cat or two reminded their companions of God's amazing world and His love for all His creatures.

PART *Teachers* ONE

God seems to know that the best way we stubborn humans learn is by example. He has sent His cats to teach us the same lesson over and over until we finally get it! We've included several pieces by Marion Bond West about her fraidy cat, Minnie, written over a period of years. Minnie remains timid and shy, but her fear reminds Marion that there is One to Whom she can turn in moments of need.

Glenn Kittler has learned a lot about communication from his Louie. We all need to be touched and acknowledged—a lesson Louie frequently reminds Glen about.

Here are cats who have jobs, who insinuate themselves into our lives, who worry us and who won't be ignored. And there are cats who come into our lives to remind us, as Phyllis Hobe discovers, that God answers our prayers— even those about cats—if only we remember to ask and understand He will answer in His own time.

As you read of these feline companions, we know you'll learn something, too—about relationships, understanding, and God's love for us all.

Minnie: Teaching by Example

by Marion Bond West

My husband Gene and I know what to expect a few moments after we go to bed and turn off the light. It has become a nightly routine. Our ten-year-old cat Minnie, who isn't very courageous, will pad softly into our room, hesitate for a few moments, then spring gently onto our bed. She settles down in between our feet. I suppose because it's dark and still, she thinks we don't know she's there. But usually one of us says, "Hello, Minnie. We know it's you. You're welcome to come and sleep with us. You don't have to sneak in after the light is off."

Still, she comes only when it's dark and our voices have quieted. *Poor Minnie. She needs to become more...bold*, I thought, one night just before I drifted off to sleep. Then my eyes popped open. Another thought came quietly, but defiantly. *I would like for you to come to Me, child, without such hesitancy, also. Sometimes you come almost apologetically, wondering if you'll be received. Come to Me, boldly.*

Right then and there, I approached my Father with a problem I had thought too small to bring to Him. In my mind, I sat in His lap like a small child and explained, "It's income tax time again,

Father. I've procrastinated long enough. In the morning, will You help me to organize what my husband has asked me to do?"

And then I turned over and went to sleep. I liked the sound of Minnie purring at the foot of our bed.

Minnie reminds me of myself. There are times when I am overwhelmed with the idea that somehow God has forgotten about me and has left me behind. Sometimes trusting Him is nearly impossible for me. And then I look at Minnie.

Minnie was abandoned several times as a kitten before we got her. The experience was evidently so traumatic that the fear of being abandoned still rules her life. When my husband Gene and I plan a trip, she sits and sadly watches us pack. We tell her that we will be back soon and that Patty, a neighbor-friend, who loves her dearly, will be coming to feed and care for her.

Still, the fear is very deep. Sometimes she sneaks inside the open suitcase or curls up on the clothes carefully laid out on the bed.

One day, when I was packing, Minnie crept into the room and gave me that "Are-you-leaving-me-again?" look. I knelt down, looked directly into her wild, yellow eyes and said, "Minnie, we aren't ever going to forsake you. We'll be back. You'd be a much happier cat if you could learn to trust us."

And as I said those words I seemed to hear a whisper in my heart: *You'd be a much happier person if you could learn to trust Me, Marion. I will never leave thee, nor forsake thee.*

Sound advice, I thought, *for a cat and cat lover.*

Minnie is the ultimate "'fraidy cat." Everything that moves scares her. She's the most cautious, suspicious creature I've ever known.

She won't leave the house unless I'm with her, and even then, a falling leaf can send her scurrying back inside.

We knew some adjusting would be in order when we got a golden retriever/Labrador puppy for Christmas. Lovey wasn't much of a threat when she was six weeks old and lived in a backroom. But we knew there would be trouble when she got older. So we moved her outside to a newly built, roomy pen.

The new arrangement seemed to be working well for all of us. Then one day Lovey escaped, and all eighty pounds of her pushed the backdoor open unexpectedly, looking for someone to play with. She galloped toward Minnie, who was enjoying a leisurely late breakfast. The cat got one quick glimpse of something behind her, coming hard and fast, and took off for her favorite hiding place—underneath our unusually low bed. She remained there for almost three days, refusing food or water or affection.

When Minnie finally came out, she'd developed a peculiar fear: She was now horrified of her tail! Invariably, she'd glance over her shoulder and see her tail as she'd seen Lovey. Then the tail would start jerking. She'd spit at it and hiss at it and try to claw it, only to end up running frantically to get away from it. Often when "the tail began to chase the cat," I'd scoop her up in my arms, hold her tail completely still and speak in a soothing voice. "Minnie, your silly tail is nothing to be afraid of. Anyway, I'm here to protect you. Don't run anymore. Stand still, girl."

Sometimes I let things chase me around, just like poor Minnie. Things like fear and "what ifs" often chase me into an emotional tailspin. Now I say, *Marion, don't let fear or your imagination chase you around again. Remember, your Father is your protector. Stand still, girl.*

Communicating

by Glenn Kittler

When I was a new cat owner, I read a newspaper article claiming that household pets, especially those that did not go outdoors, adjusted to the routines of their owners. Any sudden change of routine on the part of the owner could cause the animal to become upset or withdrawn. Working at home as I do, I thought that I spent plenty of time with my pet. But during some weeks my schedule was irregular and my cat would grow unusually quiet and distant. The article stated that when this kind of reaction occurred, the owner should explain the situation to the animal. Although the pet would not understand, at least it would not feel abandoned. I followed the article's advice—and it worked!

Late one afternoon I was preparing to leave my apartment with a visitor. I went over to my cat, who was perched on his favorite chair "Now, Louie," I said, bending down to his level, "Mr. Davidson and I are going out for something to eat. You have everything you need so you take care of the apartment and I'll be back sound ten o'clock and I'll tell you all about it."

"What in the world are you doing?" my friend gasped. I told him about the newspaper article. He asked, "And that works?"

I nodded.

Halfway through dinner my friend said, "I've been thinking about you and your cat. Wouldn't it be nice if people communicated with one another like that? There would be less hurt, less argument, less pouting, less misunderstanding," I thoroughly agreed with him.

When I arrived home that night, Louie was waiting for me just inside the door. He arched his back and rubbed against my legs, purring all the while. I began to tell him about my evening. Yes, indeed, my friend was right. Would that we humans could learn the art of communicating with one another. Love and understanding would surely follow.

Recently I attended a large cultural gathering of mostly strangers. I saw people greeting one another with smiles and handshakes, hugs and kisses and an occasional touch to an arm or a pat on the back.

I probably wouldn't have given it a thought except that I heard a woman nearby say, "Have you noticed how people are always touching each other?"

The woman with her said, "Yes, I have. Why do you ask?"

"I don't like it," the first woman said. "Somehow it just seems like an empty gesture. It's meaningless."

Then I thought of Louie. People unfamiliar with the ways of cats may not believe this, but my cat Louie is a real toucher. He was about a month old when he moved in with me. Once he discovered where at home I work and spend most of my day, he decided to join me, curling up under the desk and resting his head on my foot. When I get up and move about, Louie follows me, and when I go back to my desk, her curls up again and puts his head back on top of my foot.

This has been going on now for ten years. No matter where I happen to be in the apartment, Louie is there too, touching me with a paw or brushing against me. I don't know whether he does this to let me know he is there or to be sure I am there, but I do know that I like it. And it gently tells me I'm wanted and needed.

No, a touch isn't an empty or meaningless gesture, it's a silent way of letting the heart say what really doesn't need to be said.

Doing God's Work

by Edward Grinnan

As part of the hectic swarm of office workers making their way down Madison Avenue every morning, I pass a little flower shop on the west side of the street. In the window there usually lounges a big, fat, fluffy, indolent-looking cat colored like agate. There are days when I've wanted to shake this smug creature by the scruff of his neck and tell him to make himself useful.

One particular Friday recently, when I was feeling harried and behind, as if the week had skidded by without my getting anything useful done, I found myself stopping to glare through the window at this puffy loafer. There he was, flat on his back in a pool of appropriated sunlight, legs splayed, a furry mockery of the work ethic. "You good for nothing..." I started to mutter when an elderly woman, immaculately dressed, appeared at my side. "Yes, isn't he wonderful?" she said. "I love to watch him enjoy his rest after a night of chasing mice."

"He doesn't look as if he's chased a mouse in his life," I snorted.

"On the contrary," she shot back. "I know the owners of this shop. They had a terrible problem with mice until they got Clancy. He saved their necks!"

I continued on my way down Madison, but slowly, giving some thought to what she'd said. I'd been hasty about the big cat, letting my own aggravations color my perceptions. How often did I do that with other people, friends and colleagues, even strangers? After all, as the woman pointed out, God has given all of us a job to do, even Clancy. I should remember that.

A Cat Named Sweetie

by Richard H. Schneider

Perhaps my antagonism toward cats dated from the time I used to chase them from my father's fish pool with a garden hose. To me, cats were snooty creatures with an insouciant air of independence, not at all like good-hearted dogs, who slavered for attention and practically somersaulted for a pat on the head.

When my younger son Kit carried in a gray-and-white kitten he had found, I reluctantly accepted the new addition. Kit and his brother Peter named her Sweetie, and she soon made friends with our two dachshunds. But the cat and I were not close.

Everything changed when we moved to a small farm in northern Virginia, where Sweetie enjoyed roaming our barn and nearby field. One evening we returned from shopping to hear a plaintive cry from the barnyard. Out of the shadows came Sweetie, crawling on her belly. Kit picked her up and cried, "She's been hurt!"

Her lower legs were in bloody shreds. Evidently she had been bushwhacked by a sickle from someone mowing the adjacent field. We called a local veterinarian, who said to bring her by in the morning. "She'll be dead long before that," gasped my wife Betty.

We called a friend, who suggested a big-animal vet in nearby

Leesburg. Although the vet was tending a sick horse at the time, he said to bring our cat right over.

Kit drove while I held Sweetie on my lap, cushioning her on a towel. As the headlights cut through the black trees lining the small dirt road, I found myself talking to Sweetie, praying for her and gently rubbing between her shoulder blades with my thumb. That seemed to soothe her.

The vet, William Rokus, met us at the door of his office. He was a giant man dressed in khaki, with hands the size of hams. What could *he* do for our pitiful bundle of fur?

The man gently took Sweetie, gave her a shot that knocked her out and then sat down to work while Kit and I watched. An aura of compassion emanated from the huge man as he worked ever so patiently and carefully, those big hands expertly wielding suture and needle as he deftly stitched Sweetie's shredded paws and legs. Finally he handed me the cat, gave us instructions and medication and told us that he thought Sweetie just might make it.

We drove home in silence. The next morning we coddled Sweetie, fed her warm milk and stroked her fur. Again I found myself rubbing her between the shoulder blades, and she cocked her head to squint up at me.

In a few days Sweetie was clumping around on plaster casts, and before long she was limping on paws that looked remarkably normal, thanks to the skill of William Rokus.

Soon Sweetie was patrolling the barn again, but she never returned to the field. When an engine started up, she streaked from sight. She always had a slight limp, but it never seemed to bother her. When we moved to New York she became a city cat, reigning over her yard and hissing off any creature that had the audacity to edge close.

But some kind of bond had been struck between Sweetie and me that night. When I read the paper or worked at my typewriter, a warm bundle of fur sprang into my lap to rest and purr. At night she curled on my pillow against my head.

Sweetie lived for sixteen years, quite old for a cat. It has been a few years since she died peacefully in her sleep. But I still think of her. She taught me so much.

I learned that we should avoid prejudice, that we should not judge proficiency by appearance and that God *does* listen to our prayers for animals.

I also discovered that everyone has a need when wounded, whether it's for quiet companionship, a sympathetic word or a gentle massage between the shoulder blades.

Reality Check

by Linda Neukrug

Stripe, one of our two cats, is in love with my husband. As soon as Paul settles into his recliner at night, Stripe races to the chair, jumps up on Paul's chest and gazes up at him with an adoring expression on her face that says, "If only some cruel accident of fate hadn't made us members of a different species." And, believe, it or not, I was jealous.

The situation disturbed me so much that I waited in a long line one Saturday to explain the situation to a renowned cat expert at an ASPCA pet fair. "I even gave her some catnip. She still doesn't care for me!" I cried. "What should I do?"

I suppose I expected sympathy; I certainly expected some concrete advice (such as "feed her from your hand" or "brush her coat"). Instead, the woman stared at me for what seemed like a long moment, and then said, "Laugh!"

"Laugh?" I repeated blankly.

"You're jealous of a *cat?*" she said. "And you don't think that's funny enough to laugh about?"

I was embarrassed for a moment. And then it dawned on me—it *was* funny! So I laughed. And even though I'm still just a wee bit jealous of Stripe, I've learned to live with it.

God Takes Care

by Kathie Kania

We live next to a wooded creek in the hills of Oregon, and it's not unusual to see a hungry coyote or bobcat slinking around the perimeter of our property. We have to keep close watch on our cats and small dogs; just this summer, three neighborhood pets "disappeared."

When Squeaker-Box, my daughter Kristin's orange cat, didn't show up for breakfast one morning last week, I knew that the worst had happened. I prayed that Squeaker-Box had not been hurt too much and that she had not suffered long. I prayed that little Kristin might understand. And I prayed, too, that we'd find another kitty that could be loved as much. But did you notice that I never prayed for the obvious—the thing that would require cold, hard faith? *I never prayed that Squeaker-Box would come back!*

That's why I felt so ashamed (and relieved!) when a hungry orange cat cried at the door later that night. I had been too busy praying for things that *wouldn't* be needed.

So from now on, I'm going to try to remember to pray for the obvious, mustering up as much faith as I can. Maybe God will say, "No," maybe, "Yes." But why waste time praying all around the problem? Come to think of it, I haven't seen Squeaker-Box yet this morning. *Lord, could You please bring him home again?*

Only a Paper Cat

by Fay Angus

My husband John and I are cat people. We rest best when lulled to sleep by the rhythmic *pur-r-r* of our marmalade cat Ginger. She jumps to the foot of our bed, kneads the blankets and nuzzles up to our feet, before we turn out the light.

Imagine our shock the night that Ginger, who was not much more than a kitten, jumped onto the bed, suddenly arched her back, hissed and growled, sprang sideways and rushed out of the room. In a few minutes she came slinking back, her eyes fixed on John. Quizzically we looked at each other, then followed her gaze to the large greeting card on his nightstand—our daughter's birthday selection for John. It was the head of a Siamese cat with enormous blue, luminous eyes!

"Ginger's terrified of a paper cat," I whispered to John. "Let's take it down!"

"No!" John whispered emphatically. "She needs to find out for herself that it's only paper and won't hurt her."

For a half an hour we watched Ginger hiss and growl at the paper cat. Finally, she lunged at it with her paw, knocking it to the floor, where we left it for the night.

The next day we put the card back up. That night once again Ginger knocked it off the stand. It took several nights before she realized she had nothing to fear from the bright blue eyes of a paper cat.

Like Ginger's paper cat, so many of our fears are unfounded. For instance, I'd always been terrified of driving the tangle that is our California freeway system. "Come along, honey," my husband said to me recently. "It's really only another paper cat! You can do it." With his encouragement and with a lot of careful practice, I discovered I *could* drive the freeways without fear!

Now I quite enjoy freeway driving...as well as driving other unfounded fears away.

Cat with No Name

by Bert Clompus

The cat showed up a few days after my bookkeeper Norman told
me he was quitting. Scrawny as a frayed piece of rope and gray as
a foggy morning, she sat high atop a bale of hay in my barn,
mewing and complaining. That reminded me of how Norman had
reacted when I tried handing him a key to my hardware store so
he could open up in the morning. "I'm quitting, Bert, I can't
handle that responsibility right now," he complained. I looked at
my employee's pallid face and frowned. He disappointed me and
I told him so. But I excused him from opening up the store and let
him get back to his bookkeeping.

I wish I could have ignored Norman's refusal the way I ignored
the gray cat. I busied myself filling three bowls for the cats I already
had—Faith, Hope and Sheldon. When I was finished, the gray cat
jumped to the floor, boldly pushed Sheldon aside and began eating his food. Sheldon, who was twice her size, looked up at me
and protested. "Hey," I told him. "I can't fight your battles."

The gray intruder quickly finished Sheldon's food and shoul-
dered Faith aside to get at hers. "I bet I know where you come
from," I accused. "You come from that cat-infested old barn down
the road."

I didn't need another cat. So after she was finally satisfied, I opened the barn door and shouted, "Shoo!" But the gray cat ignored me and nonchalantly climbed back on the bale of hay. That irritated me almost as much as Norman's refusal to take the key.

The next morning the gray cat was still there, staring down at me and informing me how hungry she was. "That's tough," I snapped. I filled my cats' dishes, put them outside the barn, and left. Later, I saw she was outside, pushing my cats aside and attacking their food. And one by one my cats walked away, totally disgusted with her, as I was with Norman.

When the pushy feline finished eating, she tried making friends with my cats. She began rubbing against them, but they either walked away or batted her with their paws. I didn't blame them. Then I—and my 67-year-old temper—picked up a stone and hurled it at her. The cat scooted around the side of the barn.

Immediately I became guilt-ridden and hoped God was busy looking somewhere else. I also hoped it was the last I had seen of the little pest. But the object of my short-lived wrath cautiously peeked at me from the corner of the barn. "Okay, have it your way," I muttered. It was the same thing I had muttered to Norman.

The following morning the gray cat was first to greet me and begin her incessant chatter as she followed me into the barn. There she watched me fill the bowls. There were four now, and she hungrily tore into them. When Faith, Hope and Sheldon finally arrived I had to put more food in the dishes. "Keep this up and you'll eat me out of house and home!" I complained to the gray cat, who contentedly licked her paws. It reminded me of the way Norman had contentedly returned to his quiet world of bookkeeping for me.

But I soon began looking forward to the gray cat's early-morning greetings down by the hydrant outside the barn. And one morning, while I was retrieving the empty bowls, she quickly rubbed the back of my hand with her cheek and dashed away. It happened faster than the beat of a butterfly wing. A few days later she allowed me to pet her and, finally, hold her. She weighed next to nothing. That cat and Norman were really two of a kind. "Dear Lord," I prayed, "help me put some meat on this poor thing."

Faith, Hope and Sheldon continued to snub the gray cat, which made me more sympathetic toward her. I decided to have my vet check her out. I also intended to have her spayed. The vet told me to put her in a carrier the night before her operation.

When that night arrived, I tried putting her into the carrier, but she seemed to have grown another four legs. It was like fighting a furry octopus. She also began mewing pitifully, as though knowing what lay ahead for her. Her cries broke my heart and made me relax my grip. She got free and disappeared into the night. "Good!" I shouted after her. "I'll never see you again, and things will get back to normal around here!"

The following morning, much to my relief, she was waiting at the hydrant. I bent down to pet her, but she would have none of it. She ate with one eye on her food and one eye on me. And for good reason too—the next time I would show no mercy, and off to the vet she would go.

But my plans for the gray cat evaporated like rain on a hot sidewalk. She was finally putting on weight, but it was all in her belly. After a few days, it became obvious she was pregnant, and I knew then why she had pushed her way into my life. I only wished I knew why gentle Norman had failed me.

"Boy, you sure know how to complicate things around here," I complained to the gray cat. I was certain this would be the last straw for Faith, Hope and Sheldon, and they would pack up and leave. Nevertheless, I tried building up the pregnant cat for her coming ordeal by feeding her as much as she could consume.

The day finally came when the gray cat gave birth to three kittens in one of the stalls. Two were alive. One was gray and striped like a tiger. The other was carbon-black from the tip of its nose to the tip of its tail.

The kittens remained in the stall for a few more days and then disappeared. I looked everywhere for them, but couldn't find them. I wondered if their mother had done away with them. "Where are they?" I demanded when she showed up for her evening meal. The tired cat looked at me a second then quietly ate her food. I decided the babies were really gone and became very angry. "Okay, kitty-cat, no babies, no special treatment!" I told her, and gave her less food the next day.

But that old guilt hit me again. What if she was still feeding them somewhere? And aside from that, she was becoming so emaciated it was painful to look at her. She reminded me of Norman, who was steadily losing weight and looking so fragile he could break in half.

A week later she was in the barn waiting for me to fill her dish when something caught my eye. It was a little black head peering at me from a crack between two bales of hay. I froze and waited. A little gray head appeared too. I looked at their weary mother and shamefully conceded, "I guess I had no faith in you. I hope you'll accept my apology." I said nearly the same thing to Norman when I finally learned his sister had been stricken with Alzheimer's disease the year before, and he had been exhausting himself caring for her.

Each day I watched the gray cat pull her kittens toward her to feed them. I don't know how she did it. She became thinner and thinner, and I prayed for the day her babies would be weaned so she could rest.

Then, one day, the kittens began eating food from their mother's bowl, and the next morning the gray cat wasn't waiting at the hydrant for me. When she finally showed up she was breathing strangely and wouldn't eat. She just rested a while in the sun and then disappeared. It worried me more when she didn't show up for her evening meal. I put a bowl of food in the barn for the kittens and kept them company while they ate.

While I watched the kittens, the gray cat appeared. She rubbed against my leg as she walked slowly past me. Her eyes a bit out of focus and breathing with great difficulty, she lay down and seemed to wait. I petted her while the kittens lay next to her. Then I left them alone together.

The next morning I took a shirt from my closet and carried a shovel down to the barn, where I found what I knew I would find. I wrapped the gray cat in my shirt and buried her next to the stream winding through my property. Then I prayed the Twenty-third Psalm and, as though she could still hear me, whispered, "I loved you, gray cat."

Right then it struck me hard that I had never given her a name. I ran back to the barn and picked up her two babies. "Your name is Tiger," I told the striped kitten. "And your name is Hoppy," I said to the black one, who had a funny little walk.

As they scampered away, I thought about the gray cat, who,

like Norman, I had condemned before knowing the facts. I closed my eyes and promised God I would try breaking my awful habit of jumping to conclusions. Then I thanked Him for Norman, and for the kittens who now greeted me down at the hydrant the way their mother used to do.

Three Little Kittens

by Phyllis Hobe

In my rural area I often see barn cats hunting in the fields. In exchange for keeping the rodent population down, they get food and shelter from farmers, but they aren't comfortable with people. If they wander onto my property, they run off as soon as they see me.

One morning, however, I found a cat curled up beneath the shrubs in front of my house. It was pregnant, a pretty little gray cat with black stripes. I brought out some food, which the cat gobbled up. She let me pet her and rubbed against me, purring. This was no barn cat. It was a family pet.

I called everyone in my neighborhood, but no one had reported a missing cat. I tried the local police, the animal shelter, several veterinarians—with no success. It seemed probable she had been abandoned by her owners. It also was obvious that she was going to deliver her kittens very soon.

What was I to do? I couldn't bring her into my home because she might be diseased and infect my other pets. But it was October, and though the days were warm, the nights were cold. At sunset she let me pick her up and I took her into my garage. She curled up on a pile of old towels and at that moment she went into labor.

For the next few hours I watched in awe as the cat delivered three kittens. From what I could see they were not only alive, but vigorous. "As soon as you can, start picking them up and petting them," my veterinarian said when I called him. "That way, when you want to find homes for them they'll be ready to live with people."

Find homes for three kittens? I hadn't thought of that. I called the animal shelter, but I was told if I brought them in they would have to be put to sleep immediately. "It's the way it is," the woman told me. "The newborns and mother might have diseases our other animals could catch." There was a sadness in her voice. "If you can keep them for six weeks, when they finish nursing we can take them in then."

Six weeks, I thought. *But maybe I can find them homes before that.*

My house isn't large and I already had two cats and one dog, so I carried the mother and her kittens down to the basement and piled newspapers and old towels in a box for a nesting place. Of course, my other animals were curious, and it took some athletic maneuvering to get past them every time I used the basement door.

"Lord, I've got six weeks," I prayed. "I need all the help You can give me." I called everyone I knew and passed the word. I ran an ad in the local paper. I even told people I didn't know well and asked them to tell their friends. I kept getting the same response: People who loved cats already had one or more. *Surely*, I told myself, *someone will come forward.*

No one did. As the weeks passed I felt uneasy. Was God going to abandon the animals just the way some human had? I couldn't believe that. But the kittens—two females and a male—were getting bigger, learning how to jump and climb, and I couldn't keep them in the basement much longer. My veterinarian examined them and gave them rabies shots, so I knew they were healthy.

But when I called the animal shelter they had bad news for me. They were overwhelmed with kittens; they couldn't promise to keep them for long. *I can't let them be put to sleep.*

On the last day of the sixth week I reminded God that we had come to our deadline, yet nothing was happening. And then it hit me: I had given God an ultimatum. I had more or less told Him I would have faith in Him for six weeks and no more.

I was so ashamed. "Forgive me, Lord," I prayed. "I know You will help me find homes for these little ones. However long it takes, I'll look after them."

A sense of peace came over me. For the first time I allowed the kittens and their mother to follow me upstairs. I trusted my very friendly dog and cats to accept them, and after a bit of curious sniffing, they did.

When the kittens were eight weeks old a friend of a friend called and asked if she could see them. When she did, she fell in love with them and took one of the females home with her. Two days later I had a call from a young couple whose cat had died a month earlier. "We miss him so much," the woman said. They took the rambunctious young male with them. By the next week the third kitten went home with the young man who delivers my fuel oil.

That left the mother cat, whom I decided to keep. Like my animals, she wasn't young and spent most of her time sleeping. But then I had a call from a friend's neighbor. "I'm getting on in years and so is my cat," the woman told me. "We need some company but neither of us can keep up with a kitten. I was wondering if you would let me have the mother."

These events happened three years ago, and all four cats are doing well. As for me, I learned a valuable lesson. Now when I need God's help I simply ask, knowing He will come to my aid. And I don't give Him a deadline.

PART *Angels* TWO

We know that angels are messengers from God. We've imagined their awesome majesty, their broad wings, their shining faces. But here are some other angels— small furry ones who bring God's message loud and clear.

Debbie Blais's Dharma is sent to help her through a rough time of cancer treatment. Dharma comes at a time of need and reminds Debbie of love, affection and the wonder of life—and leaves when the message is delivered.

Mary Ann O'Roark is reminded of God's love and promise of eternal life when she comes across her oddly named cat's name—Onions—not once, but twice at a special time. Little two-year-old Kaleigh Lester's angel was simply a cat who took the girl home—a cat no one had ever seen before or since!

God's angels come in all shapes and sizes—we need only to open our hearts to His infinite love to recognize them.

Dharma, the Cat Who Took Away Fear

by Debbie Blais

Wrapping my arms across my chest, I set out for the two-block walk to the lake. I was tired and weak, but needed to get out of the house and clear my head in the cool September air. Three months earlier, in June 1995, I had been diagnosed with breast cancer. After undergoing a radical mastectomy I thought the worst was behind me, but the cancer had spread to my lymph nodes. Now I was part of an aggressive clinical-research trial that included a combination of high-dose chemotherapy and hormone-blocking drugs aimed at destroying the cancer cells and preventing a recurrence. I was thirty-seven and terrified of dying. Nightmares plagued me when I lay down to sleep.

The long, twice-monthly chemo treatments wiped me out completely for days at a stretch. Keeping down bread and water was next to impossible. My hair fell out in clumps. I suffered these side effects almost willingly. But after a particularly draining treatment this week, I had run a dangerously high fever. Death was closing in on me, and I wondered if there was any escape.

A wind blew and I reached up to keep my cap from flying off and exposing my bald head. Walking to the lake on balmy fall afternoons used to delight me, but now the way the clouds moved together and apart, the leaves fluttering in circles on the breeze, only reminded me of what I'd miss when I was gone.

I stopped at the edge of the lake and stared down at the sandy bottom. *Why is this happening, God?* A high-pitched mewling sounded from a nearby bush. I was familiar with that cry, having rescued many a stray kitten.

I can't help you, I thought sadly. *I can barely take care of myself.* I'd gotten a medical leave from my job, and my husband Gary had taken over caring for our three other cats and doing most of the housework after putting in full days at his carpentry business.

"Meow! Meow!" the pleas continued. I closed my eyes tight. Ear-splitting shrieks and squawks filled the air. I whirled around. Four blue jays were swooping down upon the bush. I shooed the birds away and carefully pulled back the tangled branches. A tiny orange tabby with bright blue eyes peered up at me, mewling like a baby. I couldn't just leave him there. I gently picked him up and held him in my palm.

"Little one, I don't know which of us is in worse shape," I said, running my fingers through the shivering kitten's fur. Maybe Gary could find him a home. I walked back to the house and collapsed on the couch. The kitty curled up on my chest, near the scar from my operation. For hours I stroked him and his purring calmed me.

"What do we have here?" Gary asked, smiling, when he came home from work.

"You know what a sucker I am for hard-luck cases," I said. "Would you take him around and see if someone wants him?"

After Gary left with the kitten, I lay down on the couch and stared at the second hand on the clock moving slowly, imperturbably around the face. Our three cats sat on the windowsill watching the deepening twilight. I found myself missing the little ball of softness that had nestled on my chest all afternoon. Finally I paged my husband. "Do you still have the kitty?" I asked when he called.

"I was just about to give him to someone."

"Don't. I need him."

When Gary brought the kitty back, he curled up on my chest again as if it were home.

The following morning the kitten purred me awake, and for the next few days he was with me round-the-clock. He loved to snuggle his face under my chin.

"What am I going to name you?" I said one night, looking down at him. He seemed to have found his place comforting me. "Is that what you're here for?" I asked, scratching the back of his neck. "Is that your purpose?" I'd read once that *dharma* is a Hindu term meaning one's purpose or place in life. "I'll call you Dharma," I decided, looking him in the eyes. *What about me, God?* I wondered. *What's my purpose?* For the time being all I wanted was to give this kitten as much love as he was giving me.

I spent the days reading, listening to inspirational tapes and participating in cancer-support groups on the Internet, with Dharma never far away. When I was exhausted, Dharma nuzzled my cheek and kept me going. He brought out in me a spirit of fun and whimsy that for months my fears had stifled. "Kiss me, Dharma," I'd say, planting one on his whiskery nose.

As he grew, he got to running through the house, clawing furniture. Shortly after one chemo treatment, I lay on the couch, weary and bored. Dharma climbed onto the armrest and began scratching it to shreds. "I think we've both got cabin fever," I told him. I brought him out to our backyard, where the other cats were playing. A flutter of yellow wings passed overhead. Dharma pawed at the air and began chasing the butterfly about the garden. His joy was infectious. I sat on the steps and laughed as he leaped and meowed among the hibiscus and jasmine and long-stemmed purple Porter's weed. Watching him made me feel I didn't have a care in the world. And to think at first I hadn't wanted to keep him!

After my last treatment in November, my doctor told me I was cancer-free. Finally I could tune back into the world.

As my strength slowly returned, I spent less time on the couch and more time on the back steps watching Dharma chase the elusive butterflies. I started doing more housework. I carried Dharma like a baby to the garage with me when I did the laundry and let him tag along when I vacuumed, his purring almost as loud as the whirring motor. "Not fair. You have a little helper," Gary joked. "I had to clean up alone." In December I had reconstructive surgery and made plans to return to work.

Three days after the surgery I opened the back door to let the cats into the backyard to play. Just before I let Dharma go I scooped him up and said, "Oh, I love you so much," kissing him as usual. He pressed his nose against my lips, kissing me back! I watched him scamper off after a butterfly before going back inside to take a nap. Scenes of Dharma romping with the butterflies filled my mind. My dreams were much more pleasant these days.

I awoke around dusk to the sound of the doorbell. I got up and saw Gary talking to a neighbor at the door. She handed him some-

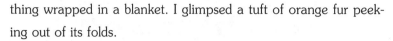

thing wrapped in a blanket. I glimpsed a tuft of orange fur peeking out of its folds.

Dharma!

Somehow he had gotten out of the backyard and been hit by a car. I couldn't believe it. "No, no," I kept saying, feeling somehow that if I said it enough, Dharma would not be lost to that great unknown that haunted me. Gary laid him down in the garden. Then he put his arms around me. "You know, Debbie," he said softly, "I think God sent you this angel to help you through a very rough time. Now that his job's done, God's brought him home."

I thought about Gary's words as he dug a small grave for Dharma near the Porter's weed. Sitting on the back steps in the cool dusk, I could still see Dharma, a blur of orange traipsing through the flowers, and felt at peace even in the midst of my grief. I knew the memories he gave me would be with me always. On the tiny headstone I wrote by hand, "Dharma, my little angel!"

He had inspired me to seek life's joy when I was at my lowest. Today, nearly three years later, not only am I cancer-free, I am also free of my paralyzing fear of death. I live each day to the utmost, as Dharma taught me—and trust God to take care of the rest.

A Gathering of Gentle Blessings

by Mary Ann O'Roark

I thought if I took a trip to a faraway place I could escape the pain of loss.

While I was leafing through the pages of a catalog from a group called Country Walkers, a trip had caught my eye. It was a week-long walking tour in Cornwall, the craggy peninsula at the south-western tip of England, where the ocean beats against rocky cliffs and beguiling ancient legends hover in the air like mist. So I signed up to join a dozen or so others and several guides; in August 1996 we would meet in the seaside town of Penzance and from there climb the coastal paths of the area that claimed King Arthur and in whose hillsides nestled the remains of prehistoric settlements and mysterious stone circles. A place so removed from my own daily life would help me get away, I hoped, from the sadness that had enveloped me.

My mother had died suddenly in the spring of 1993, and my father almost exactly a year later. Even though time had passed, I was still paralyzed by moments of grief and desolation. I longed to feel connected to my loved ones, to know that what had linked me to them was still intact.

My mother had the most beautiful singing voice I have ever heard. Everyone exclaimed about her solos at events in our West Virginia and Ohio communities. Among her favorite selections was "The Holy City," which begins, "Last night I lay a-sleeping…" and whose verses gradually build in intensity to a glorious chorus: "Jerusalem, Jerusalem, lift up your gates and sing…Hosanna in the highest…Hosanna to your king." When she and my father made their long-awaited trip to the Holy Land in the 1980s, the tour bus stopped on a hillside overlooking Old Jerusalem, and the group's leader—once the minister of our church—had asked my mother to sing the song.

As my father told me in one of his warmly eloquent letters, "Your mother sang "The Holy City" so beautifully and impressively that when she finished, the bus did not move for several minutes while most all present regained composure and dried their tears. Dr. Boak stated that he and his wife would never forget that moment and doubted if anyone present ever would either." When my mother died, "The Holy City" was sung at the conclusion of her funeral. "Hosanna in the highest…Hosanna to your king."

After our parents' deaths, life went on for my brother, sister and me. Still, the clouds of sorrow were debilitating. Then, in June 1996, the cat that had curled at my side for fifteen years retreated to a corner and refused to eat.

I had originally adopted the cat from an animal shelter; at the time the staff informed me that her name was Onions. *Onions?* For nearly a year I called her what I thought was a more suitable name; she merely stretched and ignored me. When one night, just testing, I called, "Onions?" she replied *whirr-up!* and bounded toward me. Whether I liked it or not she was clearly Onions. And so it remained—people often commenting on her unusual name—for many happy years. Until Onions became ill and I lay next to her on the floor night after night, my hand on her fur. She did not recover.

I felt it again: a jarring dislocation, an unraveling of continuity. Touchstones that had sustained me were gone. I could not be comforted.

So about six weeks after Onions died, I took a plane to London and boarded a train for the five-hour trip to Penzance. Looking at my map, I noted the peninsula toward which I traveled had been labeled "Inspirational Cornwall." Curious.

As passengers disembarked, I found myself alone in the railroad car. Suddenly the sadness was upon me again. I put my hands over my face, shaking with grief. "I need help," I said, in a voice so forceful that I startled myself. This was no polite prayer, but a bold and ferocious declaration: "I can't go on like this. I've *got* to have help."

A half hour later the train pulled into Penzance, and I stepped into a wash of pearly light and a rush of salty air. By the time I checked into a rambling seaside hotel, the Country Walkers group had already left for the cliffs. They would be back by dinnertime.

Setting off by myself to explore, I walked the cobblestone streets of the charming town, drawn back through time in the warm, salty air.

At some point I abruptly stopped and looked up. On the bluff above was a church of sand-colored limestone, edged with graceful low spires and a soaring tower. As if following a command, I began to climb toward it.

I crossed the old graveyard, where thin headstones leaned into wind that had polished the dates from their surfaces. A sign announced this was St. Mary's Church. I pulled at the wooden doors. Locked. My longing to go inside increased. Perhaps doors on the other side were open. I walked around the building and tried again.

This time the door swung inward. I stepped into the back of a sanctuary bathed in the tender glow of stained-glass windows. And then, breaking the silence, there was music from a piano and a woman started to sing: "Last night I lay a-sleeping, There came a dream so fair…"

They were the opening words of "The Holy City."

It felt as if I had been gently slapped on both cheeks and brought sharply, astonishingly, back to life. In the near-empty church the words rang clearly. The melody's power and intensity built phrase after phrase, culminating in the soaring chorus I knew so well. "Jerusalem, Jerusalem, lift up your gates and sing…"

As the verses continued I stood motionless. And in my mind and heart, with a reality every bit as solid as the granite walls and cliffs of Cornwall that had endured for centuries, I heard the voice of my mother—singing in the choir at our Steubenville church, practicing at our piano on Euclid Avenue in Weirton, thrilling the tourists in Israel. "Hosanna in the highest…Hosanna to your king."

When the song ended, the church was quiet again except for the rustle of pages as the pianist gathered his music. "The soloist will be giving a concert here later," a man in the back explained pleasantly. "We've opened the church for these few minutes so she could practice. Lucky you happened to be passing at exactly this time. Lovely, wasn't it?"

Choked by tears, I could only nod. "We'll be locking up again now," the man said. Quickly I scanned the sanctuary; I had to have *something* to take with me. Near the exit were items intended for sale, and I saw a small white book, *Prayers From The Heart*. It would be a perfect reminder of this blessed moment. Impulsively I also picked up a small blue pamphlet, put coins in the nearby box and stepped out into the sunlight.

The book felt good in my hand. And what charming drawings of a lamb, a bird, a church in the moonlight. I looked at the artist's name.

The first name was Gill. The last name was Onions.

Onions? The conjunction of such specific messages, perhaps small to some but deeply significant to me, delivered within moments of each other, struck me as so amazing that I laughed out loud. A human being whose proper, official, real-life last name was Onions?! (Later I checked British phone books to see if it was perhaps a common local name. It wasn't.)

There was a wooden table and bench in the churchyard, and I sat gazing across water turned to gold by the late-afternoon sun. After a while I looked at the pamphlet I had also gathered hastily from the vestibule. It turned out to be a compilation of prayers put together by the congregation of St. Mary's. I suppose it should have been no surprise that when I turned the pages, the first words I saw were these:

"Nothing can make up for the absence of someone we love...we must simply hold out and see it through."

Taking a deep breath, I read on. "That sounds very hard at first, but at the same time it is a great consolation, for the gap, as long as it remains unfilled, preserves the bonds between us." It was a quote from theologian Dietrich Bonhoeffer. "It is nonsense to say that God fills the gap; God doesn't fill it, but on the contrary, he keeps it empty and so helps us to keep alive our former communion with each other, even at the cost of pain."

I read on, entry after entry about the loss of loved ones speaking specifically to the ache in my heart. "Whatever we were to each other, that we still are," were the words of Henry Scott Holland, once Canon of St. Paul's Cathedral. "Call me by my old familiar name, speak to me in the easy way you always used....Play, smile, think of me. Let my name be ever the household word it always was....Life means all that it ever meant. It is the same as it ever was; there is unbroken continuity."

For perhaps an hour I sat there, letting the words sink in. Something I had read in my guidebooks came back to me: The town's name, Penzance, is from the Cornish *pen sans*, which means "holy headland." The wind was caressing and sweet, and gulls called like children. My senses were flooded with shimmering light, music, air. With life. And love that never stops.

That evening at dinner I told some of my walking companions what had happened. The next day, when we entered a small fishing village named Mousehole, one of our guides pointed to the gray stone seawall. "Look," he said quietly. "Somebody is really trying to tell you something."

In large runny letters, a villager had for some reason been moved to paint these words: "Hello, Sweet Onions."

And the waves surged against the rocks and sang the words that eased my loss and transcended time: "Hosanna. Hosanna in the highest."

God's Gift

by JoLynne Walz

Several months ago I moved eight hundred miles away from my family to start my first job after college. I loved my work. But coming home to the emptiness of the apartment I'd rented—that was no fun!

Early one morning I was wakened by what could only be the meowing of a cat—and it was close by. I got up to investigate. In the kitchen, I found the backdoor open—I was certain I'd locked it the night before—and, to my amazement, there was a tattered, green-eyed tiger cat striding imperiously around the room. Quickly I made a search of the apartment. Nothing was missing; nothing had been tampered with. Reassured, but puzzled, I knelt to pet the cat. She nuzzled against me, purring contentedly.

A few days passed, and no one in the neighborhood claimed her and no one advertised for a lost cat. By that time it would have been hard to give her up—and we clearly enjoyed each other's company.

"I guess it's safe to name you, my friend," I told her. "I'm going to call you 'Theodora.'"

That night, during my weekly phone call home, I told my mother about my new four-footed roommate.

"I'm glad you have a pet, JoLynne!" she said. "I've been worried about you being so lonely. In fact, I've been praying about it every day." And then she chuckled. "Wherever did you get that name—'Theodora'?"

"I don't know, Mom. It just came to me out of nowhere—the way she did."

What neither of us knew then—but I learned later—was the derivation of the name Theodora. It's from the Greek: *Theo*, God; *dora*, gift. Theodora the cat, like her name, God's gift!

Angelic Music?

by Katy Jenkin

One Saturday morning when the phone rang, I rushed past my son's bedroom to answer. *Lucky I even heard it*, I thought. Sixteen-year-old Tony had taken up the electric guitar and drums, and his hard rock sometimes drowned out other sounds and conversations. For months his dad and I had argued with Tony about his music, and I was reaching the end of my rope. I couldn't stand the racket, I couldn't stand the lyrics and I was worried about the influence that kind of music might have on my son. My constant prayer was for peace and quiet.

But at the moment, in a turmoil, I picked up the phone. It was my friend Kathleen, who was preparing to move to England. "I just found out that I can't take Sweets with me," she said. Sweets, her gray tabby cat of eight years, meant the world to Kathleen. "If I can't find a home for her, I don't know what will happen. Would you consider taking her in?"

Without warning, a yellow flash zipped across the countertop and landed in the butter dish. Our new kitten Missy had struck again. "Get out of there!" I yelled. Then Princess, our German shepherd, sauntered into the kitchen and cocked her head at me as if she understood my dilemma. I already had two pets. Could I handle a third? Kathleen waited for my response. "I'll think about it," I told her, hanging up the phone and surveying the butter tracks on the kitchen floor. At that moment Tony's music started upstairs again. My teeth clenched. It would be impossible to add another element to this circus.

And yet the idea nagged at me. When I broached the idea of a new cat sharing our space, my husband and son said they wouldn't mind. Once again I was going through my mental list of all the reasons why not to take Sweets when it occurred to me the decision wasn't entirely on my shoulders. "Dear God, what should I do?" I asked. Something told me to say yes.

I called Kathleen with the good news. "Oh, thank you so much, Katy. I know you two will be fast friends," she said. Then she reeled off Sweets's quirks: "She loves broccoli and classical music and—"

"Classical music?"

"Yes, believe it or not," Kathleen said. "It calms her. She purrs when it's playing."

On the day of Kathleen's departure, Tony and I went to pick up Sweets. Kathleen tearfully hugged her cat good-bye, then gave a last-minute admonition to my son: "Don't forget the classical music!"

On her arrival at our house, Missy and Princess sniffed the cat carrier and started hissing and barking. "Hey, Mom, Sweets can stay with me," Tony said. Before I could stop him, he hurried upstairs, carrying Sweets to her "safe" environment. Left to calm our pets downstairs, I didn't have the energy to intervene. I shuddered, thinking of my son's room, complete with drums, electric guitars and amplifiers. I just didn't see how this could end without more discord.

The next morning Tony rushed off to school after a brief announcement that the night had gone well for Sweets. "Don't let her out of my room, Mom," he warned. "I have it all set up for her."

Of course I had to open the door a crack to check for myself. I couldn't believe my ears. Strains of Bach floated out to greet me. An obviously contented Sweets was perched next to the radio, purring away. My son, the rock music fan, had set his radio to a classical station! I didn't realize Tony knew such music existed.

Evenings passed with Tony doing math homework to the strains of Rachmaninoff. Mornings began not with electric guitars but with violins. As the days went on, rock selections still emanated from the room from time to time, but more and more there were concertos, sonatas and symphonies.

The other animals settled down, and as I did my morning chores we all enjoyed the sound of Haydn drifting from Tony's room.

God had answered my prayer by bringing harmony to the whole household. He had sent Sweets, the cat who craved classical music.

The Calico Cure

by Kathryn T. Smith

My mother was a happy woman who never seemed to mind grow-
ing old. "But my forty-eighth year was traumatic," she often joked
with an exaggerated frown. "I became a grandmother." She didn't
let arthritis stop her from planning family picnics and trips of all
kinds. She loved fishing, gardening and bird watching—anything
to do with the outdoors.

Eventually Mother *had* to slow down, but she never lost her
good humor. In 1985, when she was in her early seventies, doctors advised a knee-joint replacement. After much thought and
prayer Mother decided to go ahead with the surgery.

While she was in the hospital she contracted a staph infection
in the new joint. With physical therapy her walking improved, but
nothing would heal the infection. Mother became withdrawn and
depressed. Our whole family prayed for a way to help her.

One day she was sitting alone in the backyard, wondering if
she'd ever feel like herself again. "Suddenly," she told us later,
"this cat was just there in the middle of the yard." It was a beautiful, long-haired calico. Must be the neighbor's, Mother assumed.
But when she called, the neighbor said her cat was asleep on the

sofa. Mother tried shooing the animal away. The cat wouldn't budge.

When she couldn't find the owner, Mother decided to make friends. "Calico," she coaxed, but the cat was shy. Finally, after being bribed with a can of tuna, the cat ventured almost within Mother's reach.

Every day after that, Calico showed up to be fed, and soon let Mother pet her. When the cat saw Mother come out the backdoor, she would run to Mother's chair. Calico would wait for her to sit down and then she'd roll over on her back and purr, begging to have her tummy scratched.

"Why does that cat get more attention than I do?" Daddy kidded.

"She never complains, that's why," Mother retorted.

Calico didn't befriend anyone else in the family. She allowed no one but Mother to touch her, which Mother found quite amusing.

Not long after Calico arrived on the scene, Mother went into the hospital for two weeks for another knee surgery to replace the infected joint, and then to a care center for two weeks more. While she was gone, Calico appeared every morning on the back step. Daddy put food out for her, but the cat wouldn't come near him. When Mother returned home in a wheelchair, Calico endured the indignity of being picked up by one of us and placed in Mother's lap. The cat had never sat in her lap before, but now she purred contentedly, as if that was where she belonged.

Calico was my mother's constant companion during that long year of recovery. "My angel of mercy," Mother called her. One day, after the doctors had pronounced her fully recovered, Mother decided the cat should have a checkup too, and made an appointment at the vet. The next morning, however, Calico was nowhere to be found.

We never saw her again, but I often think of her, our answer to prayer.

Cat Tale

by Cheryl Fister

Kaleigh, my two-year-old daughter, was fascinated with the city bus that roared up and down our block. I promised her we would take a ride on it together. Before we got a chance, I was awakened one morning by a husky woman in a transit authority uniform knocking on our door. "Is this your child?" she asked sternly. Standing next to her was Kaleigh, wearing nothing but her diaper. I held her tight as the bus driver and I pieced together what had happened.

Apparently my daughter had gotten up early, unlocked the front door and toddled down the alleyway to the bus stop. "I asked her where she lived, but she didn't know," the bus driver said. Then an orange cat appeared on the sidewalk. "Your daughter called, 'Kitty, Kitty,' and followed the cat right up to your front porch."

I thanked the bus driver for bringing Kaleigh home. "Thank your cat," she said.

But we didn't own a cat. Nor had I ever seen an orange one in our neighborhood.

Following Mama Cat

by Cleveland S. Baker

I'm a cat person from way back. In 1931, when I was eight years old, I lived with my grandparents on a tobacco and cotton farm in South Carolina. There was no one my age for company, so my best friend was a lovable solid-gray cat, known simply as Mama Cat. I would have been lonely without Mama Cat, and I loved her as much, I imagined, as she loved her two kittens.

The farm was located on a dirt road, and that year the state highway department began expanding it to become part of U.S. Highway 301. The tough work was done by mules towing large shovellike devices. My grandfather gave the highway department permission to dig a huge well on his property to provide water for the animals. It was four times larger than an average farm well and sat adjacent to the barn where the tobacco was dried. Granddaddy told me to be careful when I worked around it.

My job was to help bring the tobacco in from the fields and ready the leaves for drying in the barn. My hands would quickly become coated with a black tarry substance—probably one reason I have never smoked.

After the harvest was complete, there wasn't much to do while the leaves dried, which took almost a week. On one of the off days, Mama Cat and her kittens were nowhere to be found. I was disappointed. A short time later I had the strangest urge to take a walk in the field next to the barn, not something I usually did. To me, the tobacco field meant work. I was more content wandering the nearby swamp, rattlesnakes and water moccasins nothwithstanding. But this day the tobacco field beckoned irresistibly.

As I stepped among the stripped tobacco stalks, Mama Cat suddenly ran toward me meowing loudly. Then she darted in the opposite direction, looking back as if she wanted me to follow her, which I did. She led me directly to the well. Afraid to look inside the dank, dark pit, I asked God not to let me find anything too scary. Holding on, I peered over the edge. The kittens! They were trapped on a bank of dirt surrounding the water at the bottom. I immediately summoned Granddaddy, and my playmates were rescued unharmed.

Was it an angel's silent urgings that persuaded me to take a walk in the tobacco field? Mama Cat would never have come to me near the swamp, which was much too dangerous for my four-footed friend. In the years since, I have known and loved many cats, but none ever displayed the behavior of Mama Cat that day. Maybe the same angel that persuaded me persuaded her, too.

God's Silent Messenger

by Mary Mauren

Mourning was always a strange word to me—full of images of thick black veils, dirgelike music and faces blank with forced-march resignation. When our twelve-year-old son Lawrence, died in a boating accident, our family was plunged into that world of mourning, and I was suddenly living out those images. I *felt* that thick black veil covering my bleeding heart. There was a dirge too—the unanswered questions, the pain-filled memories that kept the wound open. Though I had tried to walk hand-in-hand with God for many years, it was often agonizing effort and sometimes only pure decision that kept me going on my own forced march for my family's sake.

Perhaps the questions were the hardest part of the march. There was the day the whole family brought a garden gift to the cemetery. While my husband Ray and our other children searched for water for the plants, six-year-old Kris and I sat waiting by the graveside. I was holding tears in check, busily brushing grass clippings off the simple stone marker, when I felt a tug on my coat. "Momma, was Lawrence in that big box they put under the ground here?" I drew my son to me and rocked him in an embrace. Tears spilled over as I desperately looked to Heaven for a wise way to explain, but nothing came to light.

"Where are You, God?" I cried inside. "Help me understand, or how can I ever help these little ones?"

That night I haltingly attempted an explanation as I snuggled Kris in bed. Three others crept in to listen and ask more hard questions. "I don't get it, Mom. When God saw the boat was in trouble, why didn't He do something?" "Why did God want Lawrence with Him now?" "Am I going to die before I grow up?"

Memories, too, were so hard. There was the day that eleven-year-old Paul dug out Lawrence's trademark, his coonskin cap, to wear while riding his newly inherited bike. Seeing the flash of bike and hat going down the driveway opened the dike yet one more time. The same thing would happen when Lawrence's good friend Raelyn (who is also his sister) frequently played the tape from his last school concert. Pride and pain accompanied each flashback of Lawrence's first—and last—drum solo. Together our family avoided the silent drum set, his mitt and special blue aluminum bat and his penny collection. We had decided to set aside his "treasures" until we could decide when and how best to share them. Each question, each memory hurt so!

Weeks turned into months as I struggled through the alternatives of stoic resignation, emotional indulgence and intellectual comprehension. They were all dead ends. Then, in a remarkable way, God showed me *His* simple truth.

The healing lesson began the day my son discovered our family cat on his bed, a swelling we had noticed on the cat's forehead now an open wound. together we got Tiger wrapped in a towel and to the vet, who diagnosed a deep abscess, probably resulting from a bite in a cat fight. The wound closed over on the outside, but kept festering underneath.

As the vet explained the seriousness of Tiger's condition and the need for antibiotic treatment and surgery, I stood washed again with the pain so easily triggered since the accident. Why this poor animal? Why this additional suffering?

Though my silent cries of "Why, God? Why more now?" were usually followed by "Thy will be done," it was said more with resignation than conviction.

That theme was repeated often through the next weeks as we tried to help Tiger recover. The vet gave instructions to open the wound daily and apply antibiotic powder each time until the healing progressed from the inside out. Each day was a painful trauma as someone had to catch the cat, wrap and hold him in a towel while another "operated."

After two weeks I called the vet to vent my utter frustration. "It's not getting any better. How can a wound heal if you open it every day?" The vet calmly reminded me that we were not just opening the wound, but adding a healing antibiotic powder to it each time. He said there was no quicker way to heal an abscess that deep. We were to continue the procedure until we could see healing taking place inside to out. I hung up and cried, for I simply did not believe him.

It was another week before some slight improvement seemed to be taking place. And it was at this point I learned that one of my neighbors was moving. She was a woman who had continued to say "I am sorry your son is dead" by frequently sending over gifts from her garden and kitchen, though she had never called or come over herself.

I had not written any acknowledgment cards yet, so I thought I would walk across the street to thank Mrs. Burge before she moved. She met me at the door and invited me in with a sad smile. Tiny worry lines were etched over a face that somehow seemed much older than her fifty-odd years. We sat over tea as she apologized for never coming over after our tragedy, explaining how hard it was for her to face that particular kind of pain.

"You see," she said as she stared at the cup and saucer on her lap, "twenty years ago we lost...our only child when she was just...thirteen and..." A sob escaped her throat as she covered her face with her hands. I reached for her cup and set it on the table while struggling to free my own heart and voice. I searched for a way to respond that would not add to her hurt. For a few moments two broken-hearted mothers just sat wordlessly with each other. I did try to reach out to her with words of God's ultimate trustworthiness, but I did not seem able to comfort her. I left with a heavy heart.

Taking the long way home, I pondered it all again. Wearily I asked God if *my* broken heart could ever by whole again. The suddenly, dazzlingly, the whole situation of the cat's deep wound and slow recovery flashed before my mind. Surely, surely, that was it! For twenty years Mrs. Burge had had a festering wound—opened frequently, but evidently not filled each time with a healing substance that would have allowed healing from the inside out.

It was like the sun shining through after a hard rain, for now I knew I had a choice after all. Over the coming years the choice would not be whether to open the wound of Lawrence's tragic accident and death. That would often be beyond my power as other people or situations inevitable called forth the memory.

Rather, the choice would be each time to invite and allow God's healing love to fill the open would—submerging and washing the unanswered questions and raw edges of pain the balm of His wisdom, His comfort, His healing wholeness.

Yes, the day came when we did not need to wrap the cat, open the wound and apply the healing powder. Tiger's skin finally drew together in complete wholeness. I, too, am recognizing—almost two years after our tragedy—an inner pulling together into wholeness, a little more after each time of applying God's healing love. I am recognizing His special kind of healing taking place in me—from the inside out.

We never know when we first meet someone whether he or she might become a friend, perhaps even a best friend. We are sometimes surprised when that friend is furrier than expected.

Philip Gonzalez tells the story of his friend Ginny, a dog whose best friends are cats! Betty Miller has a cat friend who helps her with her Bible study simply by making sure she gets up on time. Caroline Miller's three cats take turns to help a young boy who simply needs a little patient love. They merely treat the new visitor the way they were treated—a fine example of the golden rule.

Each one of these stories of friendship demonstrates once again how God knows what we need—long before we ourselves do. We all need friends—sometimes we don't recognize them when they come padding into our lives.

Dog's Best Friends

by Philip Gonzalez

Not all that many years ago I would have described myself as a happy, independent guy, proud of my work as a steamfitter in New York City—a job that paid well. I biked, sometimes twenty miles a day, played handball and swam in the ocean near my place in Long Beach. At forty, I lived a bachelor's life to the fullest—no financial obligations beyond my apartment, vacations anywhere I wanted and partying with friends every night.

My pals and I were tough guys, all of us. But there was one thing they used to razz me about—my weakness for animals. It went back to when I was a kid. I took in a stray kitten at age nine and later convinced my family to adopt an old dog whose owner had died. After I moved to Long Beach I'd saved an unwanted pup from being drowned, and found a home for an ex-girlfriend's cats.

Once, on a building site in downtown Manhattan, I spotted a mother rat with a nest of babies, and I left food for her every day. "It's just a *rat*," my buddies said, but I thought of her as one of God's creatures who needed help.

I never figured I'd put myself in that category. Then, on the job one afternoon in January 1990, my heavy-denim engineer's coat got caught in a pipe-cutting machine. It chewed up my right arm, whirling me like a rag doll, pounding my head repeatedly on the concrete floor. I yelled until someone pulled the plug on the machine, and when it finally released me from its grip I was rushed to the hospital. The bones in my arm were crushed. I refused to let the doctors amputate, so they used microsurgery to save as many nerves as possible. Regular physical therapy might keep the arm from atrophying, but there were no guarantees. My hand would be practically useless, and I could eventually lose my arm.

Nearly two weeks later, wrapped in bandages and still groggy, I returned to my apartment. I sat around for days, not even changing clothes, because it was too hard. I didn't shave or get a haircut. What was the use? My buddies stopped coming by. I couldn't work, bike, play ball or swim anymore. I only went out for my therapy appointments. I had to make do on a limited disability income. The best part of my life was over. So I just gave up, on myself and God.

My neighbor Sheilah was the only loyal friend I had. She often knocked on my door, trying to cheer me. One morning she invited herself in. "You've been hanging around this apartment for a month. We're going out." Too depressed to argue, I changed clothes and managed a lopsided shave. Sheilah grumbled about my ragged appearance as we got into her car. "Next stop, the animal shelter," she announced. "You're getting a dog."

"I can't take care of myself," I said. "How can I take care of a dog?" Sheilah just smiled, and by the time we hit the parking lot I'd changed my mind. *A big, male dog. German shepherd, maybe. Purebred. A great-looking dog people will admire. Then they won't notice me.*

The shelter attendant took one look at me, a bum with his arm in a sling, and immediately suggested a cat. "A nice, easy pet," he said.

"No, a big dog," I insisted, so he showed me a Doberman, a female. "I had a male in mind," I said.

As we started to move along I noticed a smaller dog curled into a corner of the Doberman's cage. A German shepherd puppy, maybe. I started to question the attendant when the pooch struggled to its feet. Definitely not a German shepherd. It was wire-haired and peculiar-looking, unlike any dog I'd ever seen. "That one's a female too, about a year old," the attendant said. The pup had been abandoned. "Isn't she cute?" asked Sheilah. The dog limped toward me. Her shoulders were broad, but her body was long and skinny, her legs thin and crooked. She had a bright-eyed face with white eyebrows and whiskers.

"She's not for me," I said. But the little dog was very friendly, begging for my attention, licking my fingers through the bars of the cage. "That's the first time she's been on her feet since she got spayed," the attendant said.

He suggested taking her outside for a walk. "She could use the exercise," he said.

"So could you, Phil," Sheilah added. "Go ahead."

What a pair we were: the dog with stitches in her belly, me with staples in my arm. Handling the leash with my left hand was almost as awkward as shaving with it. *Can't I walk a dog anymore, God? Can't I even do that?* We'd gone only a half block when the dog sat down and looked up at me. I felt a jolt of recognition when our eyes met, as if a connection was being made. "You're going home with me," I said. I could swear she smiled.

I named her Ginny. She adjusted to my apartment right away, and I decided to introduce her to the neighborhood that first afternoon. I worried she'd be too much for me, but Ginny hobbled along beside me without pulling on her leash, perfectly behaved, as if we were old friends.

We went walking the next morning, later in the afternoon, and several times the following day. It felt good to get outside again, and I found myself looking forward to our walks. On one of our strolls Ginny got excited when she saw a small yellow cat rummaging around a garbage can. My hand tightened on the leash, but Ginny pulled free. "Stop!" I yelled. *Dogs hate cats.* Ginny dashed for the cat and I feared the worst. But I watched in amazement as Ginny began licking the homeless creature as its mother would have done. The cat licked her in return and followed us home. Ginny wagged her tail when I shared some of her dog food with her new friend.

The next morning the cat was waiting outside our door with several others. Ginny pranced around them like a proud mama. A few tagged along when Ginny and I went for our walk. My neighbors waved when they saw our little parade.

"That dog loves cats," Sheilah said one day, watching Ginny cavort with her alley-cat pals. "Why not get her a kitten of her own?" I frowned. *Another pet?* But when Ginny settled down and one of the cats curled up on her flank and fell asleep, I gave in.

Once again Sheilah and I drove to the animal shelter. Ginny came with us. At a cageful of kittens, she immediately headed for a white one, who began purring like a tiny outboard motor when Ginny started to groom her. I called the kitty Madame, and she joined our household.

Soon after, Ginny led me to a cat being abused by some neighborhood kids. We rescued her and took her home. After living on the streets she was hostile, cowering in a corner, hissing at us. Ginny patiently stayed close, giving her tongue baths when she finally ventured out of her corner. I named her Vogue, and Ginny got her to trust us, even to nap on my chest as Ginny lay by my side in the recliner.

Another time Ginny raced into an abandoned building and returned with a kitten in her mouth. The vet told us the kitten had a muscular defect and advised putting her down. We took her home, named her Topsy, and she thrived under Ginny's care.

I had adopted a dog, and she had adopted three cats. Ginny loved all cats, but she had a special affinity for those who were handicapped or lost. What I didn't realize was the change she was bringing about in me. Day by day I was getting stronger.

I slept in my recliner to keep my injured arm and hand elevated as the doctors had recommended. One night I was awakened about 1:00 A.M. Ginny was pacing excitedly in the room. Twisting around, trying to quiet her, I looked down at my right hand. I could have sworn that my fingers moved. *Impossible!* Even with all my physical therapy I hadn't been able to move my arm, and my hand had remained useless. Ginny was circling the room, happily barking as if someone else were there with us. What is it, girl?" My mother always said dogs could see angels. *If that's true*, I thought, laughing, *Ginny can see the angel who moved my fingers. Because that's about what it would take.* The cats were alert too, watching Ginny. I looked at my hand again. My fingers were definitely moving. The doctors had held out little hope of my regaining any use of them. Was I dreaming?

After a few minutes Ginny calmed down. The cats curled up and Ginny resumed her place beside me. We all fell back to sleep. The next morning I'd forgotten about my "dream." Then, when I was making coffee, my right hand moved. Just a little, but it *moved*.

At my physical therapist's later that day I excitedly told her about my hand. "Impossible," she said. "Watch this," I countered, and started moving my fingers. She brought a doctor in, and I moved my fingers again. "Maybe the nerves are starting to reattach themselves," the therapist said. They gave me a new brace and assigned special exercises to strengthen my fingers. Today I've regained some use of my hand, and my arm no longer hangs limp at my side.

Ginny continues being a kind of angel to needy cats, rescuing more than three hundred at last count. We have nine sharing our apartment, and scores more who show up on the doorstep for regular meals. I count myself as one of the strays Ginny found and nursed back to health—with help, perhaps, from an angel from heaven.

Bible Study Partner

by Betty Miller

I joined a Bible study group, only to discover that between my responsibilities at home and on the job I never had enough hours in my week to finish the assignments. I tried getting up earlier, but I only found myself turning off the alarm and going back to sleep. *God, I want to study Your Word,* I prayed. *I just don't know how I'm going to find room in my schedule.*

Around the same time, a skinny, gray-striped cat appeared at my kitchen window. I couldn't let the poor thing go hungry, so I fed him. Pretty soon he was showing up every evening for supper. One night, after a heavy snowstorm, the cat didn't make his regular mealtime. Worried, I slept restlessly.

Then, just before daybreak I was awakened by a noise coming from the kitchen. I ran to the window. There, peering back at me, was a familiar, whiskered face!

Ever since, Cato the cat and I have had a new schedule. Every morning, he wakes me up at 4:30 A.M., clamoring for breakfast. After I feed him I sit down with a cup of coffee and my Bible. Thanks to my four-footed alarm clock, I have plenty of time.

Partners with God

by Kenneth Chafin

I grew up on a farm, loving animals, especially dogs and cats. I can still remember the delight of watching my cousin spray milk in the cat's mouth as he milked the cow, and the thrill of going to see Uncle Lawrence, who had promised me the pick of the litter for my first pup. But you didn't keep those pets in the house. And when they got sick, you didn't take them to the vet. Times have changed.

A few years ago, when our daughter Nancy bought her first house in Houston, an urban cat came with it. She named it Porch Cat and began putting food out for her. Porch Cat later gave birth to two kittens, which were named Peter Wyatt and Emma Louise. Then Porch Cat disappeared. Nancy put food out for the kittens, and when she discovered they were sick, she took them to the veterinarian. When Peter Wyatt died of a host of complications, it was like a death in our family. Despite her allergies, Nancy determined that Emma Louise would not suffer the same fate, and so moved her into the house. There have been many trips to the vet during the past year, but Emma is now a healthy, contented member of the family and even gets remembered with gifts at Christmas.

Out of my Great Depression background, I once said to Nancy, "Please don't tell me how much you have spent on Emma." My wife Barbara and I both know that it's probably more than we spent on Nancy during her first year, but we also agree that it has enriched Nancy's life as well as saving Emma's. There is something about caring for a cat or dog, or feeding wild birds in winter, or nurturing a plant, that makes us partners with God.

Lately, I've been thinking about getting a Jack Russell terrier. I may even keep it in the house!

Sharing

by Marion Bond West

I was overjoyed when my husband Gene surprised me with a beautiful Persian area rug. For years I had admired them and wished that one day I could own one. It was perfect in front of our fireplace, picking up the dark green, beige and rose colors of our living room. As we stood admiring it, our cat Minnie stepped cautiously onto the plush rug and settled down in the center of a bouquet of pale pink roses.

"No!" I raised my voice. Our dear Minnie was surprised because she had unlimited access to every square inch of our house, and now I was trying to train her to respect this one bit of space. That night I got up to find Minnie back on the rug, sleeping on the roses once again. I scolded her, and she left reluctantly. Perhaps I *was* a bit overprotective, but for now, while the rug was brand-new, I didn't want to risk it getting soiled.

Then, very early one morning. I came downstairs and discovered that Minnie had positioned herself so that the tips of her front paws barely touched the fringe of the rug; the rest of her was safely not touching it at all! She looked at me very innocently and pitifully, purring, as if to say, "Surely you can't object to this!"

Well, I finally felt a little silly. Minnie just wanted a soft, comfortable spot to nap, and she seemed to enjoy those pink roses. After all, this wasn't a museum, but a living room, a room to live in. How could I turn away anyone, human or animal, seeking safety and warmth?

"It's okay, girl," I assured Minnie. She purred with her eyes closed and her paws barely touching the fringe of the new rug she so loved. I went back to bed...happily...and drifted off to sleep thinking: *In any contest of wills between humans and felines, I know who usually wins.* Sleep came quickly.

Two Days and Three Cats

by Caroline Miller

When fifteen-year-old Adam* arrived at our house that winter day, I knew right away he was going to be more of a challenge than the first two troubled teens we had hosted. Even though his head was down and his shoulders slumped, there was an air of defiance about him. Adam responded with grunts when introduced to my thirteen-year-old son Rick and our cats. Dropping his bags on the bedroom floor, he crawled onto the bed and stared out the window.

After my husband's death and my oldest son's departure to college three years before, my two remaining kids and I had decided to make use of the extra bedroom by signing on with a local social service agency. We took in teenagers needing a place to stay for short periods while they were working out difficult family situations. Our first two placements had been fun and rewarding for us all. By the time Adam arrived, my daughter had gone off to college also, leaving just Rick, me and our three cats at home.

As I made supper I mentally reviewed what the agency had told me about Adam. He felt he was being pushed out of his mother's

*Name has been changed

life, unwanted, ever since she had remarried. When his mother gave birth to a boy, Adam became withdrawn. His stepfather was a nice guy, so Adam turned his anger and frustration inward. His home and school life became a disaster.

When dinner was ready I knocked on his door. No response. After knocking again, I peeked inside. Adam was lying on top of the bedspread, eyes open, bags still packed, and no lights on. He didn't reply to "Dinner is ready," so I put on a lamp and left him alone. After dinner I checked again, but nothing had changed except that one of the cats was lying next to Adam on the bed.

"Adam, you *must* be hungry. Can I bring you a sandwich?"

He nodded.

Just before retiring I looked in on him again. He was still rooted to the bed with the cat, but the sandwich and milk were gone. *Maybe things will be better tomorrow*, I thought.

They weren't. The only change was that a different cat had joined Adam on the bed. He shook his head at my attempts to get him up for school.

I can outlast him, I thought determinedly. *I'll win him over yet!* I brought him juice and toast for breakfast. No comment, no acknowledgment, but the plate and glass were empty a few hours later.

I began to get concerned and a little bit angry that afternoon when there was still no change. Nonetheless, the cats continued taking turns on the bed with him. They seemed enchanted with him.

That evening Rick's youth group met at church, which included dinner. I had planned to go with him since it was my turn to wash dishes. When I asked Adam to come along, he shook his head.

Wearily I made him another sandwich and left it along with some cookies and milk.

In the car on the way to church Rick asked, "How long is Adam going to stay with us?"

"After I call the agency tomorrow, they'll probably pick him up. I think he's past any help we can give him."

Rick was silent for a moment, then said, "I think Adam deserves the same consideration we gave Andre."

"The cat?" I asked, dumbfounded. "What do you mean by that?"

"Remember how when we adopted Andre a couple of years ago you put food and water out and told us kids to leave him alone, he would come to us when he was good and ready?" Rick continued. "It seems fair to give Adam the same consideration as the cat. It's been only two days, and it took the cat four or five before he came around."

I had to admit he had a point. "Okay, we'll give Adam a few more days to get used to us," I reassured Rick.

At church Rick asked the youth leader to pray for Adam. I began to dread what we would find at home. But when we walked through the door, Adam was sitting on the couch, eating an apple and watching television as if he had been a member of our household for years.

"I hope it's okay that I took a shower and put away my clothes," he said.

Within the week, Adam opened up. He returned to school and did his homework. Soon he and Rick were like brothers. And at least one of the cats slept on his bed at night.

A week before Adam was to return home, the placement agency called. "Adam's psychologist said he's ready to go home now," the woman informed me. "She said he must have been with a special family."

"Yep," I told her, "around here we treat kids every bit as well as we do our cats."

Love One Another

by Scott Walker

Our two cats Tuxedo and Tiger have been with us for a long time. Born in the same litter twelve years ago, they have moved with us through three states and have watched as three children have been born into our family. These cats are special members of our clan, though they have always lived outside. Fiercely independent, they roam their territory and fight their battles, but they are always home for supper.

Their appetites appear to have doubled, too. Now they stay around the back and meow for food every time the door is opened. Strangely, they often beg loudest when their bowls are brimming over with their favorite food. At first, such behavior perplexed me. For a while, I thought they might be having a problem with parasites, but our veterinarian assured me that was not the case. Then one day the explanation became perfectly clear to me.

The only time I had ever been able to pet these independent felines was when they were preoccupied eating. But once they left their food bowls, they were impossible to catch. All of their lives, these cats have associated petting with eating. So now, when they want more affection, they feel that they have to be to be fed in order to be petted.

I guess people are the same way. As a pastor, I hear a lot of folks complain about many things. But behind most of the laments, there is a deep hunger to be loved and appreciated. Wise is the person who can see through the crazy ways people ask to be stroked and then simply give them a pat on the head or a warm embrace. After all, they are not really hungry. Their plates are full. They are simply in need of love.

Friends of the Family

by Carol Knapp

One drab January day I brought home a perky black-and-white kitten who quickly batted away our midwinter blahs. We named her Sneakers for her white paws and her habit of pouncing on us from out of nowhere.

By September Sneakers had a boyfriend serenading her nightly beneath our window. He was a muscular fellow whose nasal croon would have caused heartburn in Nashville! A few weeks later Sneakers' bulging sides gave her away. She was expecting kittens. We hit upon the idea of guessing how many she would have and on which day.

Thanksgiving weekend Sneakers walked into the kitchen looking...thin. The hunt was on for the kittens. We found them, four clusters of black fluff, hidden under the covers in our daughter's bed.

Several dips into the guessing jar revealed the winners (cheers) and losers (groans). I set the date for our "Kitten Celebration." We began with Garfield the cat's favorite dinner, lasagne by candlelight. For dessert everyone unwrapped a chocolate wafer candy bar. The winners (and losers—I'm a softie!) opened small gifts relating to cats. What fun we shared around the table that evening celebrating our kittens...and ourselves.

It really doesn't take much to etch a joyful scene on a family's "memory pane." Just a trace of creativity, a dot of time, a stroke of love—and that scene will sparkle for years to come!

Why don't we do it more often?

The Cat Who Wouldn't Come Out

by Christine Conti

When my next-door neighbor Sally begged me to take in a homeless cat, I was almost ready to end our friendship.

I was tired of flea-ridden animals with sad eyes and dirty coats.
I had adopted, rehabilitated and found homes for more of them
than I cared to admit. I was just getting reacquainted with my own
neglected cats and planning my return to daily prayer and Bible
study when Sally showed up. She sat on my couch staring apologetically into her coffee cup as she gave me the details.

The cat had been cherished by the Hetricks, an elderly couple
who lived down the street. The wife had entered a nursing home,
and now her husband was sick and needed care himself. They had
no children, just some in-laws who were allergic to cats and were
thinking of putting the pet in a shelter. "But people don't go to
shelters looking for twelve-year-old cats," Sally said. "She'll be
destroyed. I'd take her, but my cat Maggie hates other cats. Yours,
though, are used to strangers."

"Well, sort of," I said. It had only taken a week for them to
emerge from under the bed when I brought the last stray home. I
smiled at Sally and thought about moving.

"Her name's Ebony," she said. "She's black with a splash of white on her chest."

"Oh, all right," I said, as if this were the deciding point. "I'll take her, but just till I find her another home." Actually, it was the plight of the elderly couple that moved me: I often wondered who would care for my animals if someday I couldn't.

Sally and I made plans to meet the cat-allergic in-laws who were temporarily caring for the Hetricks' house and Ebony. Sally left, and I went upstairs to prepare an unused bedroom—cats need their own space. The room was empty except for some rolled-up carpets and boxes of winter clothes. Muttering under my breath about yet another burden, I arranged a jumble of boxes, plastic milk crates and old blankets to provide a variety of hiding and sleeping places. Then I grabbed a cat carrier and was off.

When I got to the Hetricks' house the in-laws told me Ebony had been hiding in the cellar for as long as they had been there—about two weeks. *Uh-oh*, I thought, *not a friendly cat*.

Sally and I were able to extract a cat-shaped mop of long black fur from underneath the furnace, get her into the cat carrier and release her into my upstairs room. She immediately dashed for a milk crate behind the pile of rolled-up carpets. My cats Damian and Mookie were furious and alternated between rushing the pile, hissing furiously and beating a terrified retreat to cower in my room.

Frankly I didn't feel much differently; a new cat meant more food, litter and visits to the vet. What had I been thinking?

My resentment softened when I unpacked her things. There was a well-worn, often-repaired toy mouse, a carpet in the shape and colors of a rainbow and, most heart-tugging of all, a hand-made label on her food canister that read in fancy, crayoned letters: "Ebony—Our Pride and Joy!" All my previous refugees had been unwanted and uncared for; this was a cat that had been loved.

It wasn't an easy few weeks. Ebony was so unfriendly. Except for the necessities, which she accomplished at night, Ebony wouldn't leave her crate behind the carpet, much less her room. How was I going to find a home for her? What sort of ads and signs could I write? "Aging, unfriendly cat needs loving home"?

I bought toys, tried homeopathic remedies, positioned a mirror on the floor by the doorway so she could see from inside her room that the hall outside was cat-free....Nothing worked. Mookie and Damian didn't help either—they got over their fear and hostility but avoided her room. My vet told me that Ebony might come out in a few months, or she just might stay in that room for the rest of her life. I prayed for inspiration, and an old saying popped to mind: If the mountain wouldn't come to me, I would go to the mountain. Perhaps if I spent some time in the room with Ebony every day, she'd get used to me and come out.

At first I didn't know what I'd do in there. There was no TV, radio, stereo or sewing machine, not even a chair. *I'll take in a book*, I thought. *The Bible.*

I brought a lamp into the room and perched it on a box. Then I sat next to it on the floor, resting my back against the pile of rolled-up carpets. I twisted around and reached in to Ebony's carton to pet her and say hello. Then I turned back and read Scripture and prayed. It was wonderfully peaceful, and I stayed much longer than I had intended.

The next day and the next day and the next, right after breakfast, I had my quiet time in what I had come to think of as Ebony's room. Soon it was a firm habit. I became so absorbed in reading and praying that, one day, when Ebony crept out of hiding and sat cautiously a few feet away from me, I barely noticed. When I finished my prayers, I got my first really good look at her: a solidly built, long-haired black cat with springy whiskers and a dusting of white on her chest.

It wasn't long before Ebony jumped out of her box when I appeared, purred, rolled around happily and curled up next to me while I prayed and read. One day I came across the admonition: "And let us not be weary in well doing: for in due season we shall reap, if we faint not" (Galatians 6:9). I looked at Ebony, whom I had so resented, who had made me feel so weary, and thanked God for sending her and restoring to me my quiet time.

That was three months ago. Ebony is now a permanent part of my home—though she isn't out of her room yet. But even if she never ventures into the rest of the house, I will continue to go to her. My visits there are the high point of my day—not just because of the time I spend with Ebony, though I've come to dote on her, but because of the time I spend with God.

Friends First

by Phyllis Hobe

Love puts the loved one first. Which is more important—someone you love, or *something* you love?

Christ was able to love us even when He saw the harm we could do. Sometimes we have to do the same.

My cat Mr. Jones is more than a pet. He is a sensitive companion; he finds a way to make me smile when I am down; he respects my need for quiet when it's time to work. He makes it impossible for me to feel lonely.

But every now and then Mr. Jones claws my upholstered furniture. Not out of any sense of mischief, but because he is trying to remove the thin outer shell of his nails. Cats are made that way. At one point, when Mr. Jones began to scratch a favorite chair that had just been recovered, I decided to have him de-clawed. It seemed like the sensible thing to do. Until I asked my veterinarian if there would be any pain involved.

"Of course," he said. "He'll feel as much pain as you would feel if you had your nails removed. Not during the surgery, and not after he's completely healed. But certainly in between."

I appreciated his honesty and I didn't have Mr. Jones de-clawed, I like my chair, but I love my cat. I can't subject him to pain just to keep my life orderly. Mr. Jones does his best to restrain himself, but my favorite chair now has a lived-in—or should I say *loved-in?*—look. To me it is more beautiful than ever because it reminds me of something I learned about love: It puts the loved one first.

Which is where God puts us—always.

Purr-fect Communication

by Sam Justice

Taffy, our twelve-year-old cat, doesn't ask for much—a bed box in a heated garage, food in his bowl, a pan of water and a little fellowship. I never have to walk him, comb his coat or give him baths. Nature has well endowed him to take care of these chores himself. It's just bed, board and a bit of togetherness.

Taffy can sleep almost anywhere—spread out on the side porch or under a shady bush in mild weather, or, when it's chilly, curled up on top of a garaged car or in his box. It doesn't matter whether his food is wet or dry as long as it's steady.

What really turn him on, however, is being permitted to curl up on a seat in the dinette. He's not allowed into the rest of the house because of his obnoxious habit of clawing at rugs and the backs of upholstered chairs. The crowning point of Taffy's day is to leap up on to a dinette chair, settle down and snooze peacefully. And it's even better when there's somebody around to join him. The moment anyone sits down next to him, Taffy begins to purr like a motorboat. He's just happy to be a part of the scene and as long as he has company everything's purr-fect.

Taffy has helped me to realize how important it is for all of us to have friendly souls around us. It tells us they're glad we're here, glad to be near us, enjoy our company. In other words, we are appreciated. Now I can't purr like Taffy, but I can always say, "Glad you joined me. Nice to have you."

A NOTE FROM THE EDITORS

This book was selected by the Book and Inspirational Media Division of the company that publishes *Guideposts,* a monthly magazine filled with true stories of hope and inspiration.

Guideposts is available by subscription. All you have to do is write to Guideposts, 39 Seminary Hill Road, Carmel, New York 10512. When you subscribe, each month you can count on receiving exciting new evidence of God's presence, His guidance and His limitless love for all of us.

Guideposts Books are available on the World Wide Web at www.guidepostsbooks.com. Follow our popular book of devotionals, *Daily Guideposts,* and read excerpts from some of our best-selling books. You can also send prayer requests to our Monday morning Prayer Fellowship and read stories from recent issues of our magazines, *Guideposts, Angels on Earth,* and *Guideposts for Teens.*

DUE DATE		
NOV 4 1995		
11-27-95		
201-6503		Printed in USA

HANDBOOK OF

Hazard Communication

and

OSHA Requirements

George G. Lowry and Robert C. Lowry

COMPLIANCE GUIDE FOR THE FEDERAL
"RIGHT-TO-KNOW" STANDARD

Library of Congress Cataloging in Publication Data

Lowry, George G.

Handbook of hazard communication and OSHA requirements
Bibliography: p.
Includes index.
1. Hazardous substances — Safety measures — Standards —
United States. I. Lowry, Robert C.   II. Title.
T55.3.H3L69   1985   363.1'762'0973   85-6982
ISBN 0-87371-022-3

6th Printing 1990 (UPDATE Nos. 1-3 enclosed)
5th Printing 1988 (UPDATE Nos. 1-3 enclosed)
4th Printing 1987 (UPDATE Nos. 1-3 enclosed)
3rd Printing 1986
2nd Printing 1986

LEWIS PUBLISHERS, INC.
121 South Main Street, Chelsea, Michigan 48118

PRINTED IN THE UNITED STATES OF AMERICA

HANDBOOK OF

Hazard Communication

and

OSHA Requirements

George G. Lowry and Robert C. Lowry

COMPLIANCE GUIDE FOR THE FEDERAL
"RIGHT-TO-KNOW" STANDARD

LEWIS PUBLISHERS, INC.
121 S. MAIN STREET, P.O. DRAWER 519, CHELSEA, MI 48118

George G. Lowry received a PhD in Physical Chemistry from Michigan State University and an MS in Organic Chemistry from Stanford University. He also received a BS in Chemistry from California State University at Chico, and a Certificate in Industrial Relations from the University of California.

Dr. Lowry currently is Professor of Chemistry at Western Michigan University in Kalamazoo, where he has developed a graduate level course in chemical laboratory safety. Before becoming a professor, he was an industrial research chemist for The Dow Chemical Company.

He is also a member of an American Chemical Society task force on laboratory hazardous waste disposal, and he is an independent consultant in chemical safety. In that capacity he has delivered safety instruction to industrial workers and supervisors and has served as an expert witness in liability cases involving alleged injury from chemical exposure.

Robert C. Lowry received a JD degree from Boalt Hall School of Law at the University of California at Berkeley, where he was an associate editor of *California Law Review*. He also received two BS degrees, one in economics and the other in systems engineering, from the Massachusetts Institute of Technology, where he was a National Merit Scholar.

Mr. Lowry is an attorney who specializes in regulatory law, and he is currently a member of the legal staff of the United States Postal Service in Washington, DC, where he handles cases involving rates and classifications, contracts, and consumer protection. He has worked for public interest groups as well as both public and private sector employers, including the Union Pacific Railroad Law Department, the Massachusetts Public Interest Research Group and the Police Review Commission of Berkeley, California.

WHY THIS BOOK?

Valuable examples are included. Recently added to these is UPDATE No. 2, January, 1987 (enclosure) which provides a copy of OSHA's approved MSDS Form, plus additional data.

This tome should be a big help to people in industry, such as environmental and safety engineers, industrial hygienists, medical departments, employee education managers, plant managers, personnel directors, legal departments, governmental relations offices, plant security, fire and disaster control officers, plant maintenance managers, purchasing agents and other specifiers and, in small companies, personnel managers, presidents and owners. Consultants will find this fact-packed guide provides answers to most client questions. Others who will benefit include corporate law firms, and casualty insurance companies' claims officers, loss control engineers and risk management engineers. Industrial unions may also want this volume.

NOTICE

Effective either November 25, 1985 or May 25, 1986, ALL THE FOL-
LOWING INDUSTRIES must comply with the HAZARD COMMUNI-
CATION STANDARD:

Manufacturers of:
Apparel and other Textile Products
Chemicals and Allied Products
Electrical Equipment and Supplies
Fabricated Metal Products
Food and Kindred Products
Furniture and Fixtures
Instruments and Related Products
Leather and Leather Products
Lumber and Wood Products
Machinery other than Electrical
Miscellaneous Products
Paper and Allied Products
Petroleum and Coal Products
Primary Metal Industries
Printing and Publishing
Rubber and Plastic Products
Stone, Clay and Glass Products
Textile Mill Products
Tobacco Manufacturers
Transportation Equipment

Distributors of Chemicals
Importers of Chemicals

PENALTIES for failure to comply with the *OSHA Hazard Communication Standard* are enumerated in Chapter 2.

LIST OF
FIGURES AND TABLES

FIGURES

TABLES

CONTENTS

1

4   HAZARD COMMUNICATION

PREFACE

On November 25, 1983, the Occupational Safety and Health Administration of the U.S. Department of Labor promulgated a new "Hazard Communication" standard (29 CFR 1910.1200). The purpose of this Standard (the HCS) is to

ensure that the hazards of all chemicals produced or imported by chemical manufacturers or importers are evaluated and that information concerning their hazards is transmitted to affected employers and employees within the manufacturing sector.

The HCS preempts any state law pertaining to the same subject, and applies to chemical manufacturers, importers and distributors as well as to all employers within Standard Industrial Classification (SIC) Codes 20-39. Chemical manufacturers, importers, and distributors are required to be in compliance with applicable provisions of the HCS. All manufacturers now are supposed to be in full compliance.

Many regulated firms are understandably uneasy about the HCS. In addition to the usual negative reaction to new regulations and standards, there is concern over the complexity of the regulations and the ambiguity of certain provisions.

Nevertheless, the concepts of the HCS are supported by major labor organizations as well as by major industrial groups. Although such issues as trade secrets, the effect of the preemption provision, and the exclusion of non-manufacturing sectors from coverage are currently being disputed in the courts, there seems to be little question that the essential features of the HCS will take effect as scheduled.

This book is intended to help all affected companies comply with the HCS as smoothly as possible. Contained herein are explanations of what is required, as well as recommendations of how to comply, particularly in areas where details are not spelled out in the standard itself. Numerous suggestions are given to help you identify hazardous materials in the workplace and also to help you obtain the required information. Finally, opinions are offered as to the outcome of certain questionable matters if things go as expected. These are "educated guesses" based on experience (sometimes called "expert opinions"). Still, they are opinions rather than fact and must be understood as such. Whenever you have a question regarding your legal rights and liabilities under this standard, you should consult your own attorney for interpretation of the law as it applies to your particular situation.

Chapter 1 explains some basic concepts of safety and how they relate to the HCS. Chapter 2 outlines legal responsibilities under the HCS in terms of its provisions and exemptions. Also discussed are pending challenges to the HCS, statutory penalties for noncompliance, and the relationship of the HCS to tort liability for injuries caused by hazardous chemicals. Chapters 3 through 9 discuss particular problems to be confronted and solved on the way to compliance. These include hazard identification, physical and health hazard characterization, warning label design and content, material safety data sheets, written hazard communication programs, and employee training. Chapter 10 discusses nontechnical problems facing the manufacturing employer, as well as the practical advantages to be gained through compliance.

In the end, whether your firm succeeds in adjusting smoothly to life under the Standard will often boil down to management attitudes and the quality of relations with employees. Given a positive management attitude and good labor relations, compliance should have real long-term benefits for both the firm and its employees. We hope this handbook will make it easier to enjoy those benefits—and avoid pitfalls of the Standard—than if you were left to your own devices.

George G. Lowry
Robert C. Lowry

GLOSSARY OF ABBREVIATIONS AND ACRONYMS

ACGIH: American Conference of Governmental Industrial Hygienists

ANSI: American National Standards Institute

ATF: U.S. Treasury Department's Bureau of Alcohol, Tobacco, and Firearms

BP: boiling point

CAS: Chemical Abstracts Service

CFR: Code of Federal Regulations

CNS: central nervous system

CPSC: Consumer Product Safety Commission

DOT: U.S. Department of Transportation

EPA: U.S. Environmental Protection Agency

FDA: U.S. Food and Drug Administration

FIFRA: Federal Insecticide, Fungicide, and Rodenticide Act

FP: flash point

FR: Federal Register

GI: gastrointestinal

HCS: Hazard Communication Standard (OSHA: 29 CFR 1910.1200)

IARC: International Agency for Research on Cancer

IPS: inches per second

LC50: median lethal concentration

LD50: median lethal dose

LEL: lower explosion limit (identical to LFL)
LFL: lower flammability limit
MEK: methyl ethyl ketone
mg/kg: milligrams (dose) per kilogram (body weight)
MP: melting point
MSDS: material safety data sheet
NA: North America (shipping identification number)
n/a: not available, or not applicable
NFPA: National Fire Protection Association
NTP: National Toxicology Program
OSH: Occupational Safety and Health
OSHA: Occupational Safety and Health Administration
PBB: polybrominated biphenyl
PCB: polychlorinated biphenyl
PEL: Permissible Exposure Limit (OSHA)
PPM: parts per million
PSI: pounds per square inch
RCRA: Resource Conservation and Recovery Act
RQ: reportable quantity
SIC: Standard Industrial Classification
TLV: threshold limit value (ACGIH)
UEL: upper explosion limit (identical to UFL)
UFL: upper flammability limit
UN: United Nations (shipping identification number)
USC: United States Code
VP: vapor pressure

1 THE NEED TO KNOW

Hazardous chemicals, hazardous materials, or hazardous substances, as they are variously called, have long been used for many purposes in homes, business, and industry. Often people who use such materials are unaware of specific hazardous properties, though, and what should be done to protect themselves from illness or injury that these chemicals might cause.

Most employers provide equipment to protect their employees from a material's hazards, along with some training in its use. Information about the actual hazards involved is often inadequate, though. In many cases, the employers themselves do not fully understand the nature of the hazards.

Various government bodies have recently shown increasing concern over how to present information about material hazards to employees more effectively. Late in 1983, OSHA announced its *Federal Hazard Communication Standard* (29 CFR 1910.1200), which is intended to give employees in manufacturing industries better access to information about the hazards of chemicals in the workplace.

Before considering the details of the Hazard Communication Standard (HCS) and how to comply, it is well to consider some critical ideas and definitions. These are of central importance to a good understanding of the whole subject of chemical hazard safety.

BASIC CONCEPTS OF SAFETY

When considering the question of how to make any activity safe, it is tempting to rely on the imposition, by some authority, of a set of safety rules to cover essentially all conceivable situations that could lead to

9

unsafe acts or conditions. However, as is well known to experienced observers of such matters, there is a serious flaw in such an approach.

If employees are not convinced that they are likely to be hurt if they disobey a particular safety rule, many of them will conform grudgingly, and only when they have to. Once the foreman or supervisor is out of sight, conformity with prescribed safe practices may be relaxed. This is a key factor in any realistic concept of safety. An individual does not consider a situation unsafe, and therefore will resist forced compliance with safety rules, if he or she does not believe that situation poses an unacceptable amount of risk.

A common definition of safety is "freedom from danger or harm." However, a little reflection leads most thoughtful individuals to recognize that in this sense nothing is really safe, because it isn't possible for anything to be completely free from danger or harm. This doesn't mean we must abandon the goal of safety, but it does mean we need to consider more complicated concepts if we are to deal effectively with the question.

In the following sections, these concepts are defined, and examples are given, to set the foundation for understanding the OSHA Standard and for using it most effectively.

Hazard

A hazard may be defined as any substance, situation, or condition that is capable of doing harm to human health, property, or system functioning. Note particularly that this definition does not say that the hazard will do harm, but merely that it has that capability. Also, it does not say how much harm might be done. Thus a situation or material that can only result in a slight irritation, and only under unlikely circumstances, is a hazard just as is a situation or material that can result in a fatality and that is very likely to do so. In other words, the term "hazard" does not discriminate very well about how serious a potential harm might be or how likely it is to occur.

Unfortunately, we commonly think of hazardous things as being likely to cause serious harm, but that simply is not so. Many things that the OSHA Standard defines as hazardous can only cause slight harm or irritation, and with proper precautions even that is very unlikely. This is a point that needs to be made strongly during the training required by the Standard — otherwise workers can become paranoid about perceived dangers.

Risk

Risk may be defined as a measure of the probability and severity of harm to human health, property, or system functioning. In other words, "risk" includes both a sense of how likely harm is to occur and an indication of how serious the harm is if it does occur.

The severity of a direct hit by a nuclear weapon is about as great as anything imaginable. But if there is virtually no likelihood that such a hit will ever occur, then the risk, which is a composite of the two factors, is extremely low. The severity of a minor skin irritation that vanishes within a short time is very small. If it is almost sure to occur, though, the risk may be considered greater than that of the nuclear explosion.

Risks are very difficult to evaluate in any sense that we can rate them numerically with reliability, though in some special cases ways have been devised to do just that. But we can all have our own feelings about how risky the presence of certain hazards might be. The fact that different people evaluate the risk of any particular hazard differently is natural and is the source of many problems. In some cases regulatory bodies, and even courts of law, have made an evaluation for us, but in many cases we do have some options ourselves.

Safety

Safety may be defined as a judgment of the acceptability of risks. That is, once we have estimated how risky something is, we judge for ourselves whether we consider it safe and therefore whether we will voluntarily accept the risks.

Many people feel that the risks involved in riding a motorcycle or in skydiving are unacceptable, and they do not consider such activities to be safe. For other people, the risks involved in driving or riding in an automobile without seat belts are unacceptable and they insist on using seat belts. Similar statements can be made about cigarette smoking, heavy drinking of alcohol, eating heavily salted food, working in chemical plants, etc.

In many cases, some people will judge a risk to be acceptable, and therefore the particular activity is, to them, safe; the same activity is unsafe to other people who are unwilling to accept the same risk. Sometimes the reason is a difference of judgment as to how great the risk is, and sometimes it is primarily a matter of different attitudes of how much risk is acceptable. Statistical studies seem to indicate that the American public varies in the level of risk it is willing to accept by a factor of about ten. That is, some people usually will accept risks that are about ten times as great as those that are barely acceptable to other people.

Sometimes people are unwilling to accept a situation because they mistakenly, out of ignorance, think it is much riskier than it actually is. Other times, some individuals may be willing to accept a situation because they mistakenly think it is much less risky than it actually is. A large part of the reason for the OSHA Hazard Communication Standard is to provide workers with reliable information about material hazards so they can better understand the risks and make better decisions, and thus take better precautions, regarding their own safety.

An example of risk variability that involves potential harm to property or system functioning is that of potholes in roadways. If there are only a few very small and shallow potholes on a stretch of road, the risk is small and most drivers would consider traveling there to be relatively safe. If there are many large, deep potholes on a similar stretch of roadway, the risk is very large and most drivers would consider traveling there to be unsafe. But if there are either very many small and shallow potholes, or very few large and deep potholes, then the risk would seem to be somewhere between that of the first two examples, and whether it is judged safe to the vehicle is a matter that could lead to considerable disagreement.

This example of a few large and deep potholes is analogous to such potential harm to human health as the risk of getting cancer from environmental exposure. The probability of contracting cancer from exposure to a particular chemical in the workplace is usually extremely small—much smaller than the probability of being involved in a serious automobile collision during your lifetime. However, if cancer is contracted it may be fatal, though not necessarily so, and whether to accept such exposure as safe is an individual judgment.

A judgment of what is safe in the examples given above will not be the same for all individuals. However, most people resent being placed into such a situation against their will or without their knowledge, regardless of what their decision might be if it were made freely. The idea that people should not be put in such a position is the philosophical basis for governmental regulation of workplace safety, and for certain kinds of liability law as well, particularly the doctrine of "strict liability."

Risk Management and Safety Programs

A safety program, as opposed to safety itself, has as its main goal the task of decreasing all risks to an acceptable level. From a business viewpoint, the acceptable level may be achieved when the costs of decreasing a given risk further are greater than the costs expected if the potential harm related to that risk should actually occur. In this sense, the costs incurred by the harm are usually the costs of damages awarded by courts to injured parties who bring suit, or else they are costs associated with insurance policies purchased to cover damages and legal defense fees.

This approach is known as "risk management." In the cold light of objective fiscal analysis it makes good sense. But to many people, including some corporate directors and managers, it is questionable from the ethical viewpoint because it ignores the harmful effects on people's lives. More accurately it equates human lives with dollars — a repugnant idea to many people, even though that is a basis for disability insurance and some types of business insurance.

Since the magnitude of a risk involves both the probability and severity of the associated harm, a safety program can reasonably be based on reducing either the severity or the probability, or both. A traditional approach to chemical safety that reduces both is based on the "three lines of defense":

1. Prevent the accidental release of a hazardous substance (i.e., minimize the probability of harm);
2. Prevent human exposure, if release does occur (i.e., minimize the probability of harm); and
3. Prevent the injury, if exposure does occur (i.e., minimize the severity of harm).

It is almost axiomatic to observe that if people who work with or near hazardous materials have a reasonable understanding of the properties of those materials, they will be better able, and often better motivated, to practice these three types of prevention and hence to work safely. For many years, most large chemical manufacturing companies have had safety records that are far better than overall industry averages. This is illustrated in Figures 1 and 2, showing accident incidence and severity rates for the chemical industry compared to those for the average of all industries.

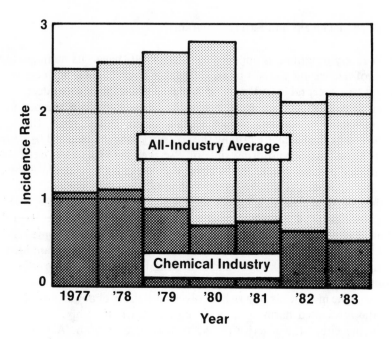

Figure 1. Industrial lost-time injury incidence rate per 100 full-time employees. Source: "Accident Facts," National Safety Council, 1978–84.

A total of 42 industrial categories were included in the studies on which these figures are based. In three of the seven years the chemical industry had the lowest incidence rate of the 42, and never did it rate poorer than fifth. In severity rates, the chemical industry ranked from second to fifth over the seven-year period, and no single industry ranked consistently better during this period. Before 1977, different classifications and reporting procedures were used, but qualitatively the same conclusions can be drawn over a period of many years.

These records have been achieved in spite of the fact that chemical industry workers are more exposed to hazardous materials than are the workers in most other industries. This probably is largely a result of better understanding of the hazardous properties by those whose main concerns are with the chemicals themselves rather than with some process or product that only incidentally involves chemicals.

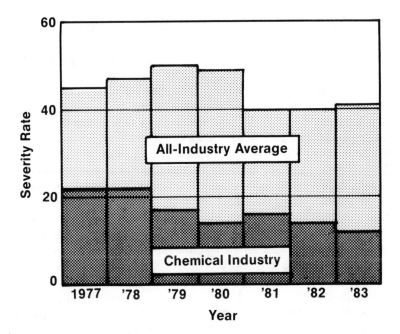

Figure 2. Industrial injury severity rate, days away from work per 100 full-time employees. Source: "Accident Facts," National Safety Council, 1978-84.

THE HAZARD COMMUNICATION STANDARD

The purpose of the Hazard Communication Standard is to remove as much as possible the mystery surrounding the risks that are due to chemical hazards in the workplace. Under other OSHA regulations, some of these risks are also regulated as to the allowed exposure level, also in line with the concepts in the last section. If these factors are kept in mind while considering the overall problems of the Standard, the "big brother is watching you" flavor of the regulations may not seem quite as distasteful.

The HCS thus requires that chemical manufacturers, importers, and distributors, and all manufacturing industry employers, institute risk management and safety programs. These programs are to inform their employees of the hazards they work with and how they can minimize both the probability and severity of potential harm. Although the Standard is aimed at enhancing safety, OSHA did not attempt to define an unacceptable level of risk. Rather the intent is to provide employees with enough information to make their own safety judgments.

The Standard covers labeling of containers, availability of material safety data sheets (MSDSs), development of a written hazard communication program, and training of employees. All these requirements are aimed at the general goal of providing employees with reliable information about the various material hazards they may meet on the job.

The HCS initially applies only to manufacturing establishments in Standard Industrial Classification (SIC) Codes 20 through 39. Surveys have shown that more than half of all the chemical-related injuries in industry occur within manufacturing firms. Thus it is expected that the greatest beneficial impact for a given amount of regulatory effort can be achieved by focusing first on the manufacturing sector. However, OSHA has indicated that the standard probably will be extended to cover other industries at a later date.

The HCS is written in rather vague language, leaving to employers the responsibility to develop the specific programs, MSDSs, labels, and training programs. Employers in most manufacturing industries are not trained in chemistry. Even if they were, most chemists are not specifically trained to recognize and deal with all the types of hazards covered. Thus, conforming with the Standard may be a serious problem for many employers.

Many small employers do not even know how to determine which of the materials they use might be hazardous. Therefore they don't know just what needs to be done. Such employers certainly are not yet ready to provide the training required by the Standard.

Maybe the identification of hazardous materials will be handled adequately for such people by the manufacturers, importers, and distributors, if they will properly conform to the Standard and provide the labels and MSDSs required. How well this will be done under the new federal requirements remains to be seen. Without such mandated procedures, though, many seem to have ignored such matters in the past.

The complete text of the OSHA Hazard Communication Standard is reprinted in Appendix 1. It describes exactly who is regulated, when, and how, but in a language that uses both bureaucratic and technical jargon. This type of language cannot be entirely avoided in regulations of this type. However, an attempt will be made here to explain the material so that industrialists who are neither chemists, health professionals, nor lawyers can understand it well enough to make life under the Standard less mysterious.

The material in the following pages, then, is designed to help employers, both large and small, in their efforts to conform with the OSHA Hazard Communication Standard with the least possible disruption of their normal operations. The ultimate purpose, of course, is to improve the protection of the health and safety of the employees. It is believed that this handbook can make a major contribution toward attaining that goal.

2 LEGAL RESPONSIBILITIES

An important distinction regarding the Hazard Communication Standard (HCS) is that it is called a "Standard," rather than a "Rule" or a "Regulation." As such, it has certain preemptive properties under Section 18 of the Occupational Safety and Health Act. That is, once it takes effect, it has precedence over any state-enacted "right-to-know" laws, which will then have to be rescinded, at least insofar as they deal with manufacturers and their employees.

Those states that have approved state OSHA plans (Table 1) must establish standards equivalent to this one. If there are compelling local circumstances that may not have been anticipated in the federal rule, the state laws may differ from the federal standard provided they are at least

Table 1. Jurisdictions Having Approved State OSHA Plans[a]

Alaska	Maryland	South Carolina
Arizona	Michigan	Tennessee
California	Minnesota	Utah
Connecticut	Nevada	Vermont
Hawaii	New Mexico	Virgin Islands
Indiana	North Carolina	Virginia
Iowa	Oregon	Washington
Kentucky	Puerto Rico	Wyoming

[a]Status as of February, 1985. In several of these states, the state plan has standards that differ in some way from the federal Standard. The state of New York also has an approved OSHA plan, but it applies only to state and local government employees.

as effective as the federal standard and that the local provisions do not interfere with interstate commerce. This provision, though, is only valid for the state-plan states. In all other states, existing laws covering the same subject matter as this Standard are to be removed from the books, and the federal Hazard Communication Standard will apply without change.

To determine the exact nature of the status of this Standard relative to local laws, you should consult your own attorney. Several aspects of the coverage may change on rather short notice.

PROVISIONS OF THE STANDARD

The first step in preparing to comply with the HCS is to determine which provisions apply to your particular firm. Figure 3 is a decision tree designed to assist you in making this determination.

The material hazards included are listed in Table 2. Sometimes it will be easy to determine whether a particular material is hazardous; in other cases it may be rather difficult. Chapters 3, 4, and 5 provide specific help on these questions in more detail. Table 3 lists the industries impacted by the HCS.

This regulation became effective on November 25, 1985 for chemical manufacturers, importers, and distributors, and on May 25, 1986 for all manufacturing industry employers ("all manufacturers").

Provisions Applicable to Chemical Industry

If your firm manufactures, distributes, or imports covered materials, you must do the following: determine which chemicals are regulated, and design and use proper warning labels. Further guidance on this matter is provided in Chapter 6.

Developing Material Safety Data Sheets

You will also need to develop Material Safety Data Sheets (MSDSs) for all hazardous materials you sell. OSHA has not specified a form for the MSDS. Its design is left to the firm, provided it contains all the information required (details of this are included in Chapter 7). In all the Federal

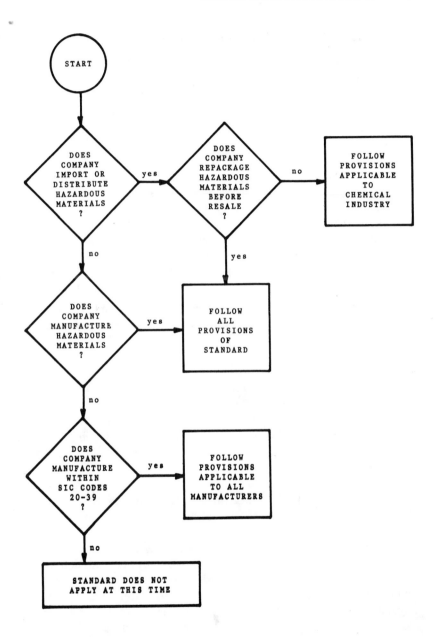

Figure 3. Determination of applicable portion of standard.

Table 2. Material Hazards Included in the Standard[a]

Physical Hazards	Health Hazards
Combustible liquids	Irritants
Flammable aerosols	Cutaneous hazards
Flammable gases	Toxic agents
Flammable liquids	Highly toxic agents
Flammable solids	Corrosive materials
Oxidizers	Eye hazards
Pyrophoric materials	Agents that act on the blood
Compressed gases	Sensitizers
Explosives	Carcinogens
Organic peroxides	Reproductive toxins
Unstable materials	Hepatotoxins
Water-reactive materials	Nephrotoxins
	Neurotoxins
	Agents that damage the lungs

[a]An estimated 70,000 to 80,000 commercial materials have one or more of these hazardous characteristics.

Regulations, the only MSDS form shown is Form 20, which was designed specifically for the shipbuilding industry and is not appropriate for general use. A copy is shown in Chapter 7. Several items required by this Standard are not included in Form 20, so it cannot legally be used in the HCS without major revision. A suitable form to use is illustrated in Appendix 2 OSHA's approved MSDS form is now part of UPDATE No. 2 (enclosure).

Chemical manufacturers and distributors come under the regulations a full six months ahead of manufacturers so that the required labels and MSDSs will be available for transmittal downstream to all affected companies by the time they are regulated.

Suppliers must assess the hazards of any materials they produce, distribute or import (whether or not repackaged). Any materials determined to be hazardous under the Standard must be properly labeled and MSDSs must be prepared. Distributors and importers may rely on the original manufacturer for the hazard determination as well as the preparation of the labels and MSDSs, or they may do these jobs themselves. The choice may depend on the company's policies regarding its company image and uniformity of treatment across the product line. All three types of firms may also contract out these tasks. Downstream employers

Table 3. Manufacturing Industries Impacted by the Standard

SIC Code	Industry Group
20	Food and kindred products
21	Tobacco manufacturers
22	Textile mill products
23	Apparel and other textile products
24	Lumber and wood products
25	Furniture and fixtures
26	Paper and allied products
27	Printing and publishing
28	Chemicals and allied products
29	Petroleum and coal products
30	Rubber and plastic products
31	Leather and leather products
32	Stone, clay and glass products
33	Primary metal industries
34	Fabricated metal products
35	Machinery, except electrical
36	Electrical equipment and supplies
37	Transportation equipment
38	Instruments and related products
39	Miscellaneous manufacturing products

who undertake an independent evaluation will assume responsibility for the adequacy and accuracy of the information they use.

Furnishing Material Safety Data Sheets

After the compliance date of November 25, 1985, the first shipment of a hazardous chemical made to a customer who is a manufacturer in SIC codes 20-39 must have properly labeled containers and must be accompanied by a copy of the MSDS for that chemical. The MSDS may be sent inside the package with the chemicals, with the shipping papers, or in a separate mailing, but it must be sent without waiting for the customer to request it. Many customers not regulated by this Standard may request copies of MSDSs, and it is suggested that they be provided automatically to all customers, to help insulate against liability suits.

Revising Material Safety Data Sheets

Whenever new hazard information relating to any of the chemicals is obtained, the MSDS must be updated within three months to include that information. The revised MSDSs must be transmitted with the next shipment to each of the regulated customers. If the chemical is not in production when the new information is received, the MSDS does not need to be revised immediately, but it must be done at the time of the first shipment when production resumes.

Provisions Applicable to All Manufacturers

All manufacturers must assess the potential hazards of all materials used in their workplace. They may do this directly, or they may rely on their suppliers to inform them of material hazards.

All manufacturers whose employees may be exposed to hazardous materials must have a complete written hazard communications program in operation (details of this program are covered in Chapter 8). The entire written program must be available for inspection upon request by employees or their designated representatives or OSHA. For this purpose, distributors who repackage hazardous material before reselling it are defined as producers and therefore must install a complete program. Importers and distributors who merely reship manufacturer-packaged materials without opening the containers are not required to include a complete program in their operations. However, it would be prudent to do so because of the ever-present possibility of accidental breakage and spills, and hence exposure to the hazards.

Hazardous Material List

The manufacturer must prepare a list of all the hazardous materials used in the workplace. For a large or complex operation, smaller lists should be made for each of the departments or areas in the plant. The written program must also include a statement as to how the hazards were assessed, which may be merely a statement that the assessments by the suppliers were relied on.

Availability of MSDSs to Employees

Copies of the MSDSs for all the hazardous materials used must be included in the written program. The lists and MSDSs must be available to all employees at all times. It is not enough to have them on file in the foreman's office unless that file is open and easily accessible to all employees at all times. It is also doubtful whether having the lists and MSDSs on a computer will meet the requirements, for two reasons. First, there is always the possibility that a computer system will be "down" for various periods of time, and then the material would not be available "at all times." Second, operation of computer terminals generally requires some training, along with regular usage to stay current, that might not be appropriate for all employees.

Training of Employees

Every manufacturer must establish a training program to ensure that the employees are aware of the provisions of the standard, that they know how to recognize the hazardous materials to which they may be exposed, what the hazards are, and how to use the materials safely. Important features of such a program are covered in Chapter 9. Such training must also be provided for maintenance, security, and other such personnel who may be exposed occasionally.

Office workers and other employees of the company who do not enter the regions of the plants where such hazards exist do not need to be included in the training plan. However, hazardous materials are used in many offices, and where they are, the employees who use them must be included in the program. Customers or other visitors do not require training, though prudent practices would seem to include provision of appropriate information to non-employees who visit the hazardous areas. A description of the training program and how it will be carried out must be included in the written program.

Contractor Training

A statement must also be included describing how the hazards will be communicated to any contractor's employees who may be working in the area occasionally. This may be fairly simple, such as a statement that a copy of the written program will be made available to the contractor and that it will be the contractor's responsibility to train his or her own workers.

Exemptions

Certain types of hazards are specifically excluded from coverage by the Hazard Communication Standard, usually because they are regulated by other agencies of the federal government.

Within the range of hazards covered, certain conditions of use are also wholly or partially excluded from coverage under one or more sections of the Standard.

Labeling Exemptions

Many items regulated by other governmental agencies have labeling requirements that are even more stringent than this Standard, and they are exempt from the labeling requirements of the Standard. However, they are still subject to the other requirements of the Standard.

Foods, food additives, drugs, or cosmetics, including flavors and fragrances, are excluded from the labeling requirements of the Standard provided that they are subject to the labeling requirements and regulations issued by the Food and Drug Administration (FDA) under the Federal Food, Drug and Cosmetic Act.

Alcoholic beverages intended for nonindustrial use are excluded from the labeling requirements of the Standard provided that they are subject to the labeling requirements and regulations issued by the Treasury Department's Bureau of Alcohol, Tobacco, and Firearms (ATF).

Consumer products or hazardous substances defined in the Consumer Product Safety Act and the Federal Hazardous Substances Act are excluded from the labeling requirements of the Standard provided that they are subject to a consumer product safety standard or labeling requirements or regulations issued by the Consumer Product Safety Commission (CPSC).

Pesticides defined in the Federal Insecticide, Fungicide, and Rodenticide Act (FIFRA) are excluded from the labeling requirements of the Standard provided that they are subject to labeling requirements or regulations issued by the EPA under FIFRA.

Process tanks and reactors whose contents may vary from batch to batch do not have to be labeled in the same way as original packages or storage tanks. The information normally required on the label must be available, but it can be in the form of placards, batch process tickets at the process control desk, or in some other way selected by the employer.

Piping does not have to be labeled within the plant. However, the information that would normally have to be included on a label must be available to the employees at all times, and some way of identifying what is in the particular pipes must be provided. This may be a piping layout diagram, or the pipes may be color coded or marked with some identifiable symbol, or any other effective method may be used.

Transfer vessels are exempt from labeling requirements under certain conditions. At all times, such vessels must be under the control of the person who originally filled them from a properly labeled container, and the label exclusion only applies for the immediate use of the material in the vessel, i.e., during the single shift involved. Thus, a foreman cannot fill a pail with a hazardous chemical and hand it to a plant worker unless the pail bears a proper label, but that same worker can fill the pail himself for his own use on the job. If the chemical is not entirely removed from the pail by the end of the shift during which it was filled, then the label requirement takes effect.

Containers of chemicals in laboratories do not have to meet the label requirements of the Standard, provided that proper labels originally on the containers cannot be defaced or removed as long as any of the chemical remains in the container. In effect, this exemption applies primarily to chemicals synthesized or in process within the laboratory itself.

Total Exemptions

Any hazardous waste as defined by the Resource Conservation and Recovery Act (RCRA) and subject to the regulations issued under that act by the Environmental Protection Agency (EPA) is specifically excluded from all aspects of the Standard. EPA regulations cover labeling, manifesting, emergency provisions and contingency plans, and employee training, so many of the same concerns addressed by the present Standard are already covered for such materials.

Tobacco and tobacco products are excluded completely from the provisions of the Standard, as are food, drugs, or cosmetics intended for personal consumption by employees.

Wood and wood products are also excluded, even when the wood is treated with hazardous preservatives and other chemicals. Most such chemicals are covered by EPA regulations and are not included in the present Standard.

Also excluded are "articles," but this exclusion is a bit more complicated and may be subject to some interpretation. An article is defined as a manufactured item which is formed to a specific shape or design during manufacture and which has end use functions dependent in whole or in part upon its shape or design during end use. The purpose of this exemption is to avoid placing a regulatory burden on articles that are in fact not hazardous during normal use. However, if the article releases, or would otherwise result in exposure to, a hazardous chemical under normal conditions of use, it is not exempted but is regulated under the Standard.

This latter provision could lead to some variability in interpretation. For example, welding rods and rosin core solder are articles according to the above definition, but welding fumes and rosin core solder fumes are hazardous substances that are specifically regulated by the Standard. Thus, it seems that welding rods and rosin core solder must be labeled, covered by MSDSs, and included in employee training and lists of hazardous materials under this Standard. Whether this will in fact be enforced remains to be seen. The same type of comments might apply to many other manufactured articles.

Mixtures/Trade Secrets

If a mixture is tested as a whole and found to be hazardous in any of the defined ways it is considered to be hazardous. Any mixture that contains at least 0.1% of a carcinogen or at least 1% of any other health hazard is considered to be a hazard and the identity of the specific hazard must be given on the label and the MSDS. Even mixtures containing smaller amounts are covered if it is reasonable to expect that vapors might be released in excess of applicable TLVs or PELs. If a mixture is not tested as a whole to determine physical hazards, evaluation of the physical hazard potential of the mixture can use any scientifically valid data that may be available.

In any mixture found to be hazardous, the identity of the compound or compounds imparting that property to the mixture must be indicated on the label and the MSDS unless exempted under the trade secret provisions of the Standard.

If the composition of a mixture is a trade secret, but the mixture is hazardous, the identity of the component producing the hazardous properties does not have to be given on the label and the MSDS, but certain other requirements still prevail. The nature of the hazard must be given, including information as to how workers can protect themselves from harm. If qualified health professionals, or OSHA, request the identity of the hazardous component for a need listed in section (i)(2) or (i)(3) of the Standard, it must be divulged under certain conditions that are designed to protect the manufacturer from losing control of his proprietary information.

Requests for the identity of hazardous components in a trade secret mixture must be in writing in non-emergency situations. The chemical manufacturer or distributor may require that emergency requests be placed in writing as soon as circumstances permit. Written requests must include a confidentiality agreement (a legally enforceable contract) that the health professional will not use the trade secret information for any purpose other than the health needs asserted, and that the information will not be released under any circumstances to anyone other than OSHA. Requests may be denied, provided the denial is also in writing and includes certain evidence and information. OSHA has established an elaborate appeals procedure to resolve such disputes as may arise. Under no circumstances will disclosure of process information or the percentage composition of a mixture be required for trade secrets.

The basic requirements for a trade secret to be protected under this Standard are that it have both secrecy and value. The identity may be a trade secret even if a competitor theoretically could discover it by analysis or in some other legal way. In order to protect the identities of trade secrets under the provisions of this Standard, it is recommended that the manufacturer of the mixture involved take the following steps:

1. Determine which specific chemical identities are in fact of critical importance to the trade secret;
2. Prepare a written justification for each specific identity classified in Step 1 (you may have to produce such a document within a short time, such as 30 days);
3. In your written justification describe how you maintain its secrecy, i.e., how you keep the identity from competitors and how you limit internal access to only those who need to know;
4. Establish the value of the secret, showing that the chemical identity results in a better product than the competitors have, or

allows the production of the same product at a lower cost than the competitors, or that it has a novel use compared to the competitors; and

5. Prepare a model confidentiality agreement permitting a health professional to have limited access to trade secret identities for legitimate purposes. This agreement should include a liquidated damages clause and a method of estimating damages in the event of unauthorized disclosure. However, note that the requirement of a penalty bond is specifically prohibited.

CHALLENGES TO THE STANDARD

At the time of this writing, several aspects of the Standard have been challenged in court, and still more challenges could be forthcoming. In addition, bills have been introduced in Congress which, if passed, could change some of the provisions of the HCS. However, any changes that might occur are not likely to render the Standard less effective, so the prudent course of action is to plan to comply fully.

Pending Litigation

On November 25, 1983, the date the Standard was first published in the Federal Register, a suit was immediately filed in the U.S. Court of Appeals for the Third Circuit [United Steelworkers of America v. Auchter (No. 83-3554)], which was later joined by New York, New Jersey, Connecticut, Massachusetts, and Illinois. New Mexico, West Virginia, the AFL-CIO and Public Citizen Inc. have also filed supporting briefs in the case. The charges in this case are summarized as follows:

1. OSHA made an arbitrary and improper decision by limiting coverage of the Standard to the manufacturing sector, thereby ignoring approximately 75% of all workers; and

2. Preemption of state and local right-to-know laws, even where the local provisions are more protective of workers, was an improper action; and

3. OSHA had improperly protected the trade secret claims by not including a provision permitting workers to challenge specious trade secret claims.

At the time of this writing, written briefs had been filed and oral arguments were scheduled to be heard on March 18, 1985 in the Third Circuit Court of Appeals in Philadelphia. A ruling on the case may not come for at least six months thereafter, which means that some of these questions may not be decided until shortly before the Standard is to take effect. If an affected party waits for a resolution of this action, there might not be enough time remaining to achieve compliance as required.

The following three sections relate to each of the charges in the steelworkers case. They are not to be considered as legal arguments for or against the case, but rather auxiliary comments to help explain some of the issues involved.

Limited Industries

OSHA felt that it would be desirable to phase in the Standard stepwise rather than to attempt to regulate everyone at once. It is a practical matter to cover the most urgent cases first and then to expand the coverage as experience with the limited coverage makes broader coverage practical.

OSHA data summarized in the preamble to the HCS (48 FR 53285, Nov. 25, 1983) showed that although only about one quarter of workers are in the manufacturing sector of industry, about one half of all chemical source injuries and illnesses are confined to that sector. Thus, OSHA's position was that they could accomplish the most, with the greatest efficiency, by covering the manufacturing industries first. The preamble implied that coverage probably would be extended to additional industries at a later date.

In a statement made at a National Governors Association meeting on January 18, 1984, OSHA Director of Health Standards Leonard Vance stated that OSHA had not at that time taken a position on preemption of states if they should expand coverage to non-manufacturing industries. thus, at least temporarily, the door seems to have been left open for states to cover other sectors, and it is likely that some will.

Preemption of State Laws

OSHA officials have indicated that the agency would not attempt to exert any preemptive authority itself. Rather it will act as a "Friend of the Court" in support of arguments by other parties that conflicting state or local laws cannot be enforced because they are superceded by the OSHA Standard.

Meantime, two rulings have been issued that relate to this matter. Administrative law judge Gerald Winerman of the California Occupational Safety and Health Appeals Board ruled against Miller Brewing Company, Irwindale (Docket No. 83-1308) in stating that California's right-to-know regulations are not preempted by the OSHA Hazard Communication Standard, at least until the latter's effective date. The defendant in this case had argued that the California law did not apply in certain of its features because of the preemption.

Both the extent and the limits of preemption under the HCS were tested in *New Jersey State Chamber of Commerce v. Hughey,* 600 F. Supp. 606 (D.N.J. Jan. 3, 1985). Various plaintiffs argued that the HCS did not preempt the New Jersey Worker and Community Right to Know Act, which applied to all employers and required the disclosure of information to both employees and the surrounding community. Judge Dickinson R. Debevoise, however, made the following relevant holdings:

1. The HCS is a "standard" under the OSH Act and not a "rule" or "regulation." Thus, the preemption provisions of section 18 of the Act, 29 USC 667(b), apply.
2. The HCS was "in effect" for preemption purposes as soon as it was issued on Nov. 25, 1983.
3. The preemption provisions of the HCS do not apply to non-manufacturing sectors, but the *entire* New Jersey Act, including those provisions applicable outside the workplace, was preempted in SIC Codes 20-39, which cover all manufacturing industries.

Judge Debevoise concluded that, since the New Jersey act had not been approved by the Secretary of Labor, it may not be enforced in SIC Codes 20-39.

Trade Secrets

The definition of a trade secret in this Standard is very similar to definitions used elsewhere: A trade secret is any confidential formula, pattern, process, device, information or compilation of information (including chemical name or other unique chemical identifier) that is used in an employer's business, and that gives the employer an opportunity to obtain an advantage over competitors who do not know or use it.

The main issues here seem to be as follows. Employers fear that making composition of secret formulas available to employees would negate their attempts to maintain the secrecy, and they would therefore lose the competitive advantage they had enjoyed. However, unions fear that trade secret exemptions would allow employers to withhold vital information from their employees.

This section of the Standard was the result of much compromise between associations of employers and those of employees. The negotiations leading to the compromise held up publication for many months beyond the time when the rest of the Standard was ready. These compromise provisions seem to protect both groups to some degree, even though neither is really satisfied.

Pending Legislation

Preemption of State Laws

New Jersey, among other non-state-plan states, joined the Steelworkers in their suit against the Standard. One of their main concerns is that they want to regulate workers' rights-to-know in a stricter way than the OSHA HCS but cannot do so if the preemption clause holds up.

On February 6, 1985, Representative James J. Florio (D-NJ) introduced a bill, HR 963. This bill would amend the Occupational Safety and Health Act to prohibit federal preemption of any state worker right-to-know law which is more protective of worker safety and health than "applicable OSHA standards," regardless of whether the state has an OSHA-approved state plan or not.

The fate of this kind of bill is very much in question. There will probably be heavy lobbying on both sides by well-financed interests. Even if the bill does pass, it too could be challenged in court, especially if it fails to protect against interference with interstate commerce. Thus, if it allows states to impose their own labeling and MSDS requirements that are different from the federal HCS, chemical manufacturers would consider it to interfere with interstate commerce.

Community Right-to-Know

In the wake of the methyl isocyanate disaster in Bhopal India on December 3, 1984, Representative Florio introduced another bill on February 6, 1985. Known as the proposed Chemical Manufacturing Safety Act of 1985, HR 965 is a national "community right-to-know" act regarding chemical hazards. Companies making or using, or proposing to make or use, hazardous materials would be required to disclose hazard information to the neighboring communities.

Some states, including New York, are already moving in this direction through legislation and administrative action. This is fraught with difficulty for industry and most likely will be subject to vigorous lobbying opposition. Unfortunately, attention is likely to be diverted from substantive issues through mutual distrust and lack of understanding.

STATUTORY PENALTIES FOR NONCOMPLIANCE

The Hazard Communication Standard was issued under the authority of the Occupational Safety and Health Act (the OSH Act, 29 USC 651-78). The OSH Act sets requirements with regard to violations of "any standard, rule, or order," such as the HCS, issued under its authority.

An inspector who discovers such a violation is required to issue a citation. The OSH Act also establishes rules for the proper conduct of OSHA inspections and enforcement proceedings. If your firm is cited by OSHA for a violation of the HCS, you may want to consult an attorney concerning your rights in the case.

For minor violations, each citation is to be accompanied by a penalty which may include a fine of up to $1,000. For more serious violations, the penalties vary up to that for a willful repeat violation which results in the death of an employee. Such a case carries a mandatory penalty of up to $20,000 or one year in jail, or both.

THE HCS AND LIABILITY IN TORT

Aside from the possibility of OSHA citations, how well you comply with the Standard can affect your firm's potential liability in tort. If employees or consumers were to be injured by exposure to hazardous chemicals used in your operations, you could become the defendant in a liability suit.

Tort liability generally is the result of finding that a person or firm is in some way responsible for an injury to the health or property of one or more other persons. The type of responsibility involved may vary depending on the relationship between the parties and the nature of their activities. If the firm or person fails to exercise reasonable care under the circumstances, i.e., fails to be as careful as any prudent person might be expected to be, then the defendant might be found guilty of negligence. Even if negligence is not proven, the defendant could still be found guilty of strict liability, i.e., he or she failed to avoid causing injury even though neither intent nor negligence was involved.

If liability is proven in court, then damages may be awarded, normally by a jury. Such damages usually involve remuneration of the cost of the injury suffered, and they may involve punitive damages as well, particularly in negligence liability cases.

How well your firm complies with the HCS can have an influence on your tort liability in two ways: (1) it can influence a decision as to what your responsibility is in terms of guarding against the injury of another party; and (2) it can influence a judgment as to how well you meet that responsibility. The exact details of this relationship will depend on all the facts of a particular situation, as well as the law of your jurisdiction. The general descriptions which follow should therefore be viewed as background information only. Specific questions should be addressed to your own attorney.

Manufacturing Employers' Liability to Employees

Many employees are covered by workers' compensation plans which provide an exclusive remedy for job-related injuries. Unintended lapses in compliance with the HCS are not likely to affect the employer's liabilities under such a plan. Intentional noncompliance, though, may result in a suit for punitive damages, regardless of whether the injury itself was intended. Thus, a workers' compensation plan does not automatically insulate the employer from negligence suits.

For injured employees not covered by workers' compensation, any failure to comply with the HCS may create an implied proof of negligence on the part of the employer. This is particularly so since one purpose of the HCS is to ensure that employees are adequately informed of the hazards of the workplace. Even if the court does not consider the failure of compliance itself to be proof of negligence, expert witnesses will probably testify that the prevailing standard of the industry includes compliance. Failure to meet the prevailing standard of the industry in any particular situation is likely to result in a finding of negligence.

Compliance with the HCS, though, does not ensure that one will not be found to be negligent, if it can be shown that the prevailing standard of the industry is to provide more information than is actually required by OSHA. You should always be aware of prevailing standards in your industry and plan to disclose hazard information in accordance with them. In this sense, it would be prudent for employers in all industries, not just the manufacturing sector, to conduct their hazard information disclosure and training in accordance with the HCS even though they have no statutory duty to do so.

Chemical Industry's Liability to Consumers

How well your firm complies with the HCS will also affect its potential liability to consumers injured by hazardous chemical products either by negligence or by strict liability. Remember that the same firm may fill the roles of employer, manufacturer, and supplier. Because of this multiple role, sometimes employees can seek legal remedy against their employer in spite of the apparent protection from suits that is provided by workers' compensation plans.

Also remember that certain types of hazardous chemical products are exempted, either partially or completely, from the HCS because OSHA does not regulate matters that have been assigned to other agencies. This does not free the employer or supplier from a liability in tort, only from a regulatory responsibility under the HCS.

In many jurisdictions, the law of products liability does not require that the injured party be the immediate purchaser of a product. Compensation to injured parties may be required if the injury can be traced to a failure by the manufacturer or supplier to meet its responsibilities to prevent injury to others. Many jurisdictions also will require a "middleman," such as a distributor, to accept shared responsibility if the middleman should have discovered and corrected the hazardous defect before passing on the product.

Negligence liability will generally be as discussed above, except that workers' compensation does not apply to injuries to consumers.

Strict liability may result where a product contains a defective condition unreasonably dangerous to users. The fact that a product is covered by the HCS is likely to be offered as evidence that strict liability rather than negligence is the appropriate standard. Moreover, failure to comply with the HCS may be cited as evidence that a product is defective in the sense that it leaves the user with a false sense of security.

Finally, proof of compliance with the HCS again is no guarantee that strict liability will not be applied. Certain products may be deemed inherently dangerous in the sense that a user has no plausible means of defending himself from injury should a defect occur, even if he has been forewarned of the possibility. Application of this doctrine is likely to vary from one jurisdiction to another.

3   HAZARD IDENTIFICATION

Both health hazards and physical hazards are covered by the Hazard Communication Standard. Some of these hazards are potentially severe, and some are relatively mild, but all are covered equally. The first step in identifying the hazardous materials is to make a complete inventory of all the chemicals and mixtures of chemicals on the premises. The second step is to prepare a list of suspects for more detailed investigation.

CHEMICAL INVENTORY

Chemical Manufacturers and Distributors

The inventory list for detailed examination of potential hazards should include all individual chemicals, all mixtures prepared from individual chemicals or other mixtures, and the raw materials used to produce finished products. Because manufacturers or importers have the primary legal responsibility to characterize all the material hazards connected with any of their products, they must conduct an exhaustive search for hazardous properties.

If a particular product is not covered under the Standard, a form letter of disclaimer should be prepared for distribution to those customers who request it. Figure 4 illustrates such a letter for nonhazardous materials such as plastic molding products. Figure 5 is a similar letter for such articles as plastic sheet or film or insulating board, or paper, or composition building panels. Because of variations in the provisions of the HCS adopted in some state-plan states, and approved by OSHA, you should ask your attorney to check these letters of disclaimer for both your state

GEORGE LOWRY ASSOCIATES, INC.

(616) 375-4368
5878 SCENIC WAY DR., KALAMAZOO, MI 49009

March 1, 1985

{ Inside }
{ Address }
{ Here   }

Dear { Name }:

The following information is supplied in response to your
request for a Material Safety Data Sheet on our { Name
of Product }.

This material is not a listed carcinogen, does not have a
TLV value assigned, and is not previously regulated by
OSHA. Furthermore, a diligent search of the available
literature has failed to establish that this material is
hazardous under the Hazard Communication Standard as
defined in 29 CFR 1910.1200 Section (c). Hence a
Material Safety Data Sheet is not available.

Thank you for your interest in our products.

Sincerely yours,

George G. Lowry
President

Figure 4. Sample disclaimer for nonhazardous materials.

GEORGE LOWRY ASSOCIATES, INC.

(616) 375-4368
5878 SCENIC WAY DR., KALAMAZOO, MI 49009

March 1, 1985

{ Inside }
{ Address }
{ Here   }

Dear { Name }:

The following information is supplied in response to your request for a Material Safety Data Sheet on our { Name of Product }.

This item is an "article" as defined in 29 CFR 1910.1200 Section (c). Further, this article does not release or otherwise result in exposure to a hazardous chemical under the conditions of your intended use. As stated in Section (b), Subsection (5), the Hazard Communication Standard does not apply to such articles. Hence a Material Safety Data Sheet is not available.

Thank you for your interest in our products.

Sincerely yours,

George G. Lowry

Figure 5. Sample disclaimer for "articles."

and the state of destination. After this has been done, you may wish to add a sentence to the effect that you "believe that statutes and standards in { state of destination } are similar with respect to such materials."

All Manufacturers

If you are a manufacturing employer, the first step is to survey your plant to identify all possible materials that might be classified as hazardous. You will later use this survey to determine which ones are in fact hazardous, and what are the specific hazards involved. But the first step is to make an inventory from which a list of "prime suspects" will be prepared.

Examine your purchase orders for the most recent twelve-month period. (In some plants, a longer period may be more appropriate.) Include both materials that are ordered regularly, and those that are only ordered occasionally. Determine where each one is used in the plant, and note this information on the inventory. Those that prove to be hazardous will need to be listed by location anyway, so this is a chance to get that job partly done.

After your purchase order survey, walk through the plant looking for anything that might not have appeared on the recent purchase orders. This would include those materials that might have been around longer than a year, free sales samples, and materials purchased with petty cash. Add all these to your inventory, with an indication of their locations.

While conducting this in-plant survey, it is also a good idea to check for materials that are no longer in use. If any are found, dispose of them as soon as possible. Otherwise they must be included in the hazard communication program (unless they present no hazard).

Also, while making the in-plant survey pay particular attention to Department of Transportation (DOT) hazardous material labels on any drums or other containers. Some of the hazard definitions used by DOT are different from those used by OSHA, but anything classed hazardous by DOT will usually be classed as hazardous by OSHA also. The DOT class will also provide a starting point for identifying the OSHA hazard classes. Also, in recent years, some chemical suppliers have been providing hazard information on package labels in addition to what DOT requires, so look for these also.

If you regularly have hazardous waste inventories and disposal pick-ups, examine your manifest files. These will remind you of where the hazardous waste originated and will lead you to the source materials, which in many cases will be hazardous also.

Once the initial survey has been completed, ask the vendors of all the materials to send you either MSDSs or disclaimers stating that specific materials are not classified as hazardous or are not covered by the Standard. While awaiting a response from your vendors, it is a good idea to do some preliminary checking yourself.

MATERIALS COVERED BY REFERENCE

All substances already regulated by OSHA are included by reference in the Hazard Communication Standard. These substances are listed in Tables Z-1, Z-2, and Z-3 located at 29 CFR 1910.1000-1047 in the OSHA regulations. Also covered by reference are all substances listed in the latest edition of "TLVs: Threshold Limit Values for Chemical Substances . . . " published by the American Conference of Governmental Industrial Hygienists (ACGIH).

All the substances in the TLV list and in the Z-tables (between 600 and 700 of them) are listed together in Appendix 3. The employer, manufacturer, distributor, or importer still must evaluate the specific hazards associated with each substance on these source lists, however. That is, either ACGIH or OSHA or both may say that something is hazardous and that its concentration in the workplace atmosphere should be kept below a certain level, but their tables usually do not say just what the hazards are. Some substances may have several different hazardous properties, and these must all be identified.

Check your materials inventory against the list of substances in Appendix 3. Each substance appears under only one name, even though many of them have several different common names. The names given are usually the ones most often seen, but your supplier may use a different name. Any of your suspect chemicals that actually appear on this list are definitely regulated. If you don't have much background in chemistry, you should enlist the help of a chemist for this purpose.

Only the compounds listed in the OSHA Tables Z-1, Z-2, and Z-3 have an OSHA-specified limit of workplace air concentration (PEL). Also, only the substances listed in the ACGIH booklet have an assigned TLV value. The term TLV is copyrighted by ACGIH, and for anyone to assign their own value and call it a TLV, however well-intentioned that act might be, is a violation of the copyright law. If a TLV is not given, it usually means that ACGIH has not evaluated its hazard thoroughly enough to assign a TLV.

MATERIALS COVERED BY DEFINITION

All chemicals are covered by the standard if there is scientifically valid evidence that they have one or more of the characteristic properties listed in Table 2. This probably includes about seventy to eighty thousand commercial materials. The meanings of these terms are not left to a "general feeling" about them. Rather they are defined precisely; the definitions are given in Chapters 4 and 5. Further discussion of the defined hazards and how to recognize them is also included in those chapters.

Any chemical, or mixture of chemicals, can be assumed to be possibly hazardous in one or more ways. But certain groups of materials are hazardous more often than others. A list of the more likely types of these materials is given in Table 4. Any material you use that is in one or more of these categories should be considered as probably hazardous until an exhaustive search proves otherwise.

Table 4. Types of Materials that are Usually Hazardous

Adhesives	Monomers
Aerosols	Office copier chemicals
Anodizing chemicals	Paints
Battery fluids	Pesticides
Catalysts	Photographic chemicals
Cleaning agents (all types)	Photoresists
Degreasing agents	Pickling agents
Detergents	Printing inks
Duplicating machine fluids	Process chemicals
Electrolytes	Resin ingredients
Electroplating chemicals	Rubber chemicals
Etching baths	Shellacs
Foaming resins	Soaps
Foundry mold materials	Solvents
Fuels (all types)	Surfactants
Industrial oils	Varnishes
Janitorial supplies	Wastewater treatment
Lacquers	Water treatment

The presence of certain elements in the chemical names of materials will suggest the probable existence of hazards. A list of the key elements for this purpose is given in Table 5. Not all compounds containing these elements are hazardous, but many are. Also, some of the elements in Table 5 are hazardous themselves, in addition to imparting hazardous properties to compounds that contain them.

Finally, the presence of certain words and word fragments in the names of chemicals can indicate possible hazards. Table 6 is a useful list of these. Not every chemical compound whose name contains these words or word fragments is hazardous, but most are.

Table 5. Elements Whose Presence Signals Potential Hazards

Aluminum	Chromium	Manganese	Silver
Antimony	Cobalt	Mercury	Tellurium
Arsenic	Copper	Molybdenum	Thallium
Barium	Fluorine	Nickel	Tin
Beryllium	Hafnium	Platinum	Tungsten
Bromine	Indium	Rhodium	Uranium
Cadmium	Iodine	Selenium	Yttrium
Chlorine	Lead	Silicon	Zirconium

Table 6. Words and Word Fragments that Signal Potential Hazards

acid	brom	hydroxide	nitroso
acryl	caustic	isocyanate	perox
alcohol	chlor	ketone	phenol
aldehyde	chrom	mercaptan	sulfide
allyl	cyan	nitrate	thio
amine	epoxy	nitrile	vinyl
amino	ether	nitrite	
anhydride	glycol	nitro	

Thus Tables 4, 5, and 6 point to materials on your inventory list that should be considered hazard suspects. Not all hazardous materials will be located with the aid of these tables, but most will.

4 PHYSICAL HAZARD CHARACTERIZATION

Materials that have one or more of the following properties are covered by the standard: combustible liquids; flammable materials; compressed gases, whether flammable or not; explosives; organic peroxides; oxidizers; pyrophoric materials; unstable (dangerously reactive) materials; and water-reactive materials. These terms have very specific definitions, which are given below, together with examples. Physical hazards are conveniently divided between fire hazards and other physical hazards, though there is some overlap.

Probably the best sources for identification of physical hazards are the latest edition of the NFPA *Fire Protection Guide on Hazardous Materials,* and the current edition of the DOT *Hazardous Materials* book, an emergency response guidebook. In some respects the DOT book is the better of the two because it gives more complete information, but it does not include as many different substances. The NFPA book also has information on trade name materials that are not listed in the DOT book. For information on materials that might be dangerously reactive, Bretherick's *Handbook of Reactive Chemicals Hazards* is a key reference source.

In addition, a number of other references, including computer data bank services, are described in Appendix C of the Standard itself. However, you should not use computer data banks as your only source of information. Most such banks are incomplete—their data are obtained from research literature that only goes back a few years. For some materials, important information was obtained many years ago and hasn't reappeared in the more recent technical literature. Such information is missing from some computer data banks.

FIRE HAZARDS

Combustible Liquids

A combustible liquid is defined as any liquid having a flash point between 100°F (38°C) and 200°F (93°C). The flash point is the temperature above which a flame will propagate through the vapors from an ignition source to the nearby surface of the liquid. Thus, a combustible liquid presents a danger of fire at slightly elevated temperatures, but not when it is at or below a normal room temperature.

Examples of combustible liquids include 10% ethyl alcohol, jet fuel, No. 1 fuel oil, phenol, pine oil, mineral spirits, and methyl cellosolve.

If 99% (by volume) of the components in a mixture have flash points above 200°F (93°C) it is not considered combustible and does not have to be tested independently.

Flammable Aerosols

A flammable aerosol is defined as one that yields either: (1) a flame projection of more than 18 inches at full valve opening; or (2) a flame extending back to the valve at any valve opening. All aerosols are mixtures. Whether a particular aerosol is flammable often depends on the particular propellant formulation, so general examples cannot be given for this category of hazard.

Flammable Gases

A flammable gas is defined in two different ways: (1) it is a gas whose lower flammability limit (LFL) is less than 13% by volume in air; or (2) it is a gas whose upper flammability limit (UFL) is more than 12% higher than its LFL, regardless of the value of the latter.

An example that qualifies under the first definition is butane, and an example under the second definition is producer gas. NOTE: Ammonia gas will burn, but it is not classified as a flammable gas, because its LFL is 16% and its UFL is 25%, a difference of only 9%.

Flammable Liquids

A flammable liquid is defined as one whose flash point is below 100°F (38°C). That is, it presents a real fire hazard if present in open containers near a source of ignition at or below normal room temperatures.

Some examples include ethyl acetate, acetone, 95% ethyl alcohol, turpentine, and gasoline.

If at least 99% (by volume) of the components of a liquid mixture have flash points above this range, it is not considered flammable and does not have to be tested independently. This is a very conservative exception, which allows non-hazardous ratings without testing. However, many mixtures containing more than 1% of a flammable liquid have flash points above 100°F (38°C), and even some above 200°F (93°C). If in doubt, they should be tested to determine whether they have to be rated flammable or combustible.

Flammable Solids

A flammable solid is one which ignites and burns with a self-sustained flame at a rate of at least 0.1 in./sec along its major axis. This category of hazard does not include blasting agents or explosives. Examples include magnesium metal and nitrocellulose film.

Oxidizers

An oxidizer is defined as a chemical, other than a blasting agent or an explosive, that can initiate or promote combustion in other materials, thereby causing fire either of itself or through the release of oxygen or other gases. Examples include oxygen, chlorine, nitric acid, fluorine, and hydrogen peroxide.

Pyrophoric Materials

A pyrophoric material is a substance that will ignite spontaneously in air at temperatures below 130°F (54°C). Examples include white phosphorus and some catalysts used in the chemical and petroleum processing industries.

OTHER PHYSICAL HAZARDS

Compressed Gases

A compressed gas is defined in three different ways: (1) it is a confined gas or mixture of gases having an absolute pressure of at least 40 psi at 70°F (21°C); or (2) it is a confined gas or mixture of gases having an absolute pressure of at least 104 psi at 130°F (54°C); or (3) it is a liquid having a vapor pressure of at least 40 psi at 100°F (38°C).

Note that these definitions do not depend on any other properties of the gas, such as toxicity or flammability. The fact that the gas is stored under pressure results in a hazard, as it could cause harm if the storage were disrupted improperly. Examples include nitrogen, oxygen, argon, acetylene, propane, and carbon dioxide. No examples were found of liquids meeting the third definition, but it is possible that some exist.

Explosives

An explosive is any chemical that causes a sudden, almost instantaneous release of pressure, gas, and heat when subjected to shock, pressure, or high temperatures. Examples include nitroglycerine, gunpowder, and diacetyl peroxide.

Organic Peroxides

An organic peroxide is a derivative of hydrogen peroxide in which one or both hydrogen atoms have been replaced by an organic radical or radicals. This definition also covers the class of compounds known to chemists as organic hydroperoxides. Examples include methyl ethyl ketone peroxide, cumene hydroperoxide, and benzoyl peroxide.

Unstable Materials

An unstable material is a chemical which in the pure state, or as produced or transported, will vigorously polymerize, decompose, condense, or become self reactive under conditions of shock, pressure, or high temperature. Examples include benzoyl peroxide, acrylonitrile, and butadiene.

Water-Reactive Materials

A water-reactive material is a chemical that reacts with water to produce a gas that is either flammable or presents a health hazard. Some examples include acetic anhydride, sodium metal, and calcium carbide.

5 HEALTH HAZARD CHARACTERIZATION

Materials that have one or more of the following characteristic properties are covered by the Standard: irritants; cutaneous hazards; toxic agents; highly toxic agents; corrosive materials; eye hazards; agents that act on the blood or hematopoietic system; sensitizers; carcinogens; reproductive toxins; hepatotoxins; nephrotoxins; neurotoxins; and agents that damage the lungs, skin, or mucous membranes. The definitions of these terms are given below, along with examples.

The health hazards are conveniently divided between acute health hazards and chronic health hazards. Some hazards have characteristics of both, but generally they are one or the other.

The effects of acute hazards are manifested soon after a single, brief exposure. Many acute effects disappear after a time and do not linger permanently. Some may show permanent effects, and therefore can be considered both acute and chronic.

The word acute can also mean sharp or severe, as with an acute pain. However, when used to describe a hazard, the word does not imply any sense of severity—merely that it has a short-time effect.

Chronic hazards have a long-time effect, essentially permanent. Their effects may be slow to develop, and often result from repeated or continuous exposure over a long period of time.

In order to identify health hazards, the key reference is the latest edition of the *Registry of Toxic Effects of Chemical Substances* published by the U.S. Department of Health and Human Services. This book also includes references to the carcinogens listed by NTP and IARC.

A number of other references, including computer data bank services, are also described in Appendix C of the Standard itself. As with physical hazards, you should not use computer data banks as your only source of information. For some materials, important information was obtained many years ago and hasn't reappeared in the more recent technical literature. Such information is missing from some computer data banks.

ACUTE HEALTH HAZARDS

Irritants

An irritant is defined as a chemical that causes reversible inflammation at the site of contact by chemical action. Irritants are characterized by standardized skin and eye tests using albino rabbits. Examples include nitric oxide, sodium hypochlorite, stannic chloride, and ethyl alcohol.

Cutaneous Hazards

A cutaneous hazard is a material that will affect the dermal layer of the body, such as by defatting of the skin, causing rashes or skin irritation. Some examples are acetone, MEK, and chlorinated compounds.

Toxic Agents

A toxic agent is defined in three different ways. It is a substance that: (1) has an LD50 for oral doses in rats of between 50 milligrams per kilogram of body weight (mg/kg) and 500 mg/kg or (2) has an LD50 for skin in a 24-hr exposure in rabbits of between 200 mg/kg and 1000 mg/ kg or (3) has an LC50 for inhalation doses administered for one-hr duration in rats of between 200 parts per million (ppm) in air and 2000 ppm.

The terms LD50 and LC50 refer to the dose and concentration, respectively, at which one half of the test animals died, also known as the median lethal dose (and concentration). At higher doses, more than half of the animals died, and at lower doses, fewer. However, frequently the values of LD50 or LC50 given in the literature for a particular compound were measured for a different animal species than indicated in these definitions, or under different exposure rates than specified. In such cases, approximate translations can be made, but they are always subject to significant error. See Appendix 4 for a discussion of lethal dose equivalencies.

Some examples to which the first definition apply are epichlorohydrin, acrylonitrile, aniline, and 2,4-D. Examples under the second definition include epichlorohydrin and acrylonitrile. Using the third definition, some examples are ammonia, nitrogen dioxide, ethylene oxide, and boron trifluoride.

Highly Toxic Agents

A highly toxic agent is also defined in three different ways. It is a substance that has: (1) an LD50 (oral, rat) of less than 50 mg/kg; or (2) an LD50 (skin, rabbit) of less than 200 mg/kg; or (3) an LC50 (inhalation, rat) of less than 200 ppm. Examples under the first definition include Aldrin, ethyleneimine, and hydrogen cyanide. An example falling under the second definition is mustard gas, and an example of the third category is dimethylnitrosamine.

Corrosive Materials

A corrosive material is a chemical causing visible destruction of, or irreversible alterations in, living tissue at the site of contact, by chemical action. These are characterized by standardized skin tests using albino rabbits. Some examples of corrosive materials are caustic soda (sodium hydroxide), sulfuric acid, hydrofluoric acid, phenol, and boron trifluoride.

Eye Hazards

An eye hazard is a material that affects the eye or visual capacity, for example by causing conjunctivitis or corneal damage. Common types of eye hazards include organic solvents, acids, and alkalis.

Agents That Act on the Blood or Hematopoietic System

This type of agent is a substance that decreases the hemoglobin function and deprives the body tissues of oxygen. Cyanosis and loss of consciousness are typical symptoms. Examples of these materials include carbon monoxide, cyanides, metal carbonyls, nitrobenzene, hydroquinone, aniline, and arsine.

CHRONIC HEALTH HAZARDS

Sensitizers

A sensitizer is a chemical that causes a substantial portion of exposed people or animals to develop an allergic reaction in normal tissue after repeated exposure. Examples include hydroquinone, bromine, platinum compounds, isocyanates, and ozone.

Carcinogens

A carcinogen is defined as a chemical that is listed as a carcinogen in one of the following three sources: National Toxicology Program (NTP) *Annual Report on Carcinogens*, latest edition; or International Agency for Research on Cancer (IARC) *Monographs*, latest edition; or OSHA's 29 CFR 1910 subpart Z. Thus, carcinogens are in fact regulated by reference rather than by performance definition. Examples of carcinogenic materials include asbestos, benzene, beryllium, lead chromate, formaldehyde, vinyl chloride, trichloroethylene, and carbon tetrachloride.

Reproductive Toxins

A reproductive toxin is a substance that can cause birth defects or sterility. Our knowledge about reproductive toxins is more recent than that of many other health hazards and is not as extensive. It is also more difficult to obtain reliable information about such effects in humans. As a result of the uncertainties, some people recommend that pregnant women, or even all women of childbearing age, avoid any contact with any chemicals whatsoever; we never know when a common chemical will suddenly be found to be a reproductive toxin. This may seem an extreme precaution, but it is not entirely without justification. However, from a legal standpoint, it involves a balance between an exposure liability and a gender-based restriction of occupation. The decision of how to handle such questions is best left to the individual firm and its attorneys. Examples of reproductive toxins include PBBs, PCBs, selenium compounds, and vinyl chloride.

Hepatotoxins

A hepatotoxin is a chemical that can cause liver damage such as enlargement or jaundice. Examples include carbon tetrachloride, nitrosamines, vinyl chloride, chlorobenzene, trichloroethylene, chloroform, and ethyl alcohol.

Nephrotoxins

A nephrotoxin is a chemical that can cause kidney damage such as edema or proteinuria. Some examples are halogenated hydrocarbons, uranium, vinyl chloride, trichloroethylene, and ethyl alcohol.

Neurotoxins

A neurotoxin is a chemical that causes primary toxic effects on the central nervous system, such as narcosis, behavioral changes or decrease in motor functions. Common examples are mercury, carbon disulfide, ethyl alcohol, acetylene, manganese, thallium, and tetraethyl lead.

Agents That Damage the Lungs

These agents irritate the pulmonary tissue, resulting in cough, tightness in the chest, and shortness of breath. Examples include silica, asbestos, cotton fibers, coal dust, and toluene diisocyanate.

6 LABEL DESIGN AND CONTENT

Any substance that is covered either by definition or by reference must be properly labeled with a warning of known hazards. The label warning must contain information about all the hazards known to be associated with the substance. That is, not just the most common or most serious hazard must be described, but all of them. For some materials this will involve several hazards.

CONTENT

In general, the only items of information required on the labels by this Standard are (1) the identity of the material, (2) the hazard warnings, and (3) the name and address of a responsible party from whom additional information can be obtained if needed. However, OSHA has previously required (29 CFR 1910.1001-1047) specific wording on the labels of certain specific materials. A list of those materials is given in Table 7. You should consult the indicated regulation for the actual text of the required wording.

In addition to the required items, either the manufacturer or a chemical manufacturer, importer or distributor may find it desirable to add information they think might be helpful to anyone using the material. If it were used only by employees of manufacturers who are in full compliance with the Hazard Communication Standard (HCS), then theoretically nothing more would be needed, as the MSDS and the training program would suffice. Because most commercially available hazardous materials are sometimes used by others, though, the supplier might be well advised to give more information on the label. Whatever extra label-

Table 7. Substances for Which OSHA Requires Specific Wording
on Labels[a]

2-Acetylaminofluorene	4-Dimethylaminoazobenzene
Acrylonitrile	Ethyleneimine
4-Aminodiphenyl	Inorganic arsenic
Asbestos	alpha-Naphthylamine
Benzidine	beta-Naphthylamine
bis-Chloromethyl ether	4-Nitrobiphenyl
Chloromethyl methyl ether	N-Nitrosodimethylamine
1,2-Dibromo-3-chloropropane	beta-Propiolactone
3,3'-Dichlorobenzidine	Vinyl chloride

[a]29 CFR 1910.1001-1047.

ing is used, if it is visible in packages prepared for shipment it cannot be of a form that resembles DOT-required labels.

When an employee is injured by chemical exposure, a liability suit is often filed, naming as a defendant every person or firm in the chain of possession of the offending material from the original manufacturer to the ultimate user. If the judge or jury decides that the package label lacks adequate hazard information in line with "common practice at the time of manufacture," then a significant monetary award to the injured party could result.

More Detailed Information on Labels

Partly for the purpose of reducing the frequency of such cases, the American National Standards Institute has published a voluntary labeling standard (ANSI Z129.1-1982). It suggests including the following nine items on the label:

- The identity of the product or its hazardous components. This, of course, is also included in the requirements of the HCS;
- A signal word. CAUTION, WARNING, and DANGER are perhaps the most commonly used signal words, in order of increasing severity of the hazard represented. This is not required by the HCS, but probably should be included even if no other voluntary information is provided.

- A statement of the actual hazards present (required by the OSHA Standard).
- Precautionary measures to prevent physical harm when using the product, such as wearing rubber gloves, goggles or respirators.
- Instructions in case of contact or exposure, such as to induce or not to induce vomiting in case of swallowing, or to rinse with cold water.
- Antidotes to be used in case of poisoning.
- Notes to physicians as to emergency treatment recommended.
- Instructions in case of fire and spill or leak, e.g., type of fire extinguisher to be used and how to clean up spill without undue risk.
- Instructions for container handling and storage, such as to keep in a cool place, away from fires, and away from strong acids.

Note: Following this standard alone would not satisfy the OSHA HCS, as it does not include the name and address of a responsible party among the nine items.

No doubt all this information is desirable. However, there is a significant problem involved with putting too much information on a label. The average person will not read a label, even the most important part of it, if it contains too much information. The balance between too much and too little is difficult to decide. Too little information carries the risk of liability suits, and too much information carries the risk that it will not be heeded. OSHA requires that these items be included on the MSDS, which is the key information repository, and it is to be available to all employees at all times. Under these conditions, it might be better not to include all the ANSI-specified information on the label itself.

LANGUAGE

The labels must be in English, but if there is a significant number of workers who do not read or speak English well, it may be desirable to add a second label with the required information translated into the appropriate language. This may actually be required in some geographical areas. Consult your attorney about this if you are in doubt.

The statements on the label should be worded as simple as possible. A hazard warning label must be interpreted easily and quickly, without having to read excessive material to get the needed information. Thus, the wording should be simple and practical, and it should be aimed at avoiding hazards that might reasonably be expected to be a problem if handling, storage, and use are improper or are accidentally disrupted.

Because much of the American adult population can only read at the eighth grade level, and many other adults are either illiterate or functionally illiterate, hazard warning labels should use as few polysyllabic, pedantic words as is possible. Avoid such statements as "wash the affected area with copious amounts of water." Many people don't know the meaning of "copious," and even if they did, there is still a question of just how much is copious. It is better to say "wash off the material with running water for at least thirty minutes." This language is both plainer and more definite as to what to do. Law suits have been settled on the basis of whether the "copious amounts" phrase provided definite enough information to the nonchemist.

DESIGN

For quick reference, it is appropriate to use a pictorial representation of hazards, both for the protection of those workers who cannot read well and for the convenience of everyone. A graphic symbol that can be understood at a glance is more effective than the simplest sentence that gives the same information.

A suitable form of graphic symbol is the type that is specified as part of the DOT labels and placards used for shipment of hazardous materials. They have the advantage that they correspond to shipping labels already familiar to industrial personnel, and for the most part require no special training to interpret their meaning. Several symbols of this type are shown in Figure 6. Pictorial symbols can also be used to indicate recommended protective equipment, such as gloves or goggles.

Except for the "toxic" and "corrosive" symbols, these hazard symbols apply only to physical hazards, and not even to all of those. Other symbols could possibly be developed to warn of some of the other HCS-specified hazards, but it seems doubtful how useful they would be in most cases, as it is hard to imagine specific graphic symbols for such hazards as "hepatotoxins," "nephrotoxins," "mutagens," and "hematopoietic agents." Whether it is wise to use the toxic symbol for these latter hazards is very questionable.

The actual placement of such symbols on the label is a matter of design preference that probably does not make much difference in terms of effectiveness. The most obvious placement is along a horizontal bar at

Figure 6. Some graphic symbols usable on hazard warning labels.

the top or bottom edge of the label, or a vertical bar along the left or right edge of the label.

It is tempting to color code such symbols, but there are chances of misinterpretation in this, in addition to being of little value to color-blind workers. Unless the same colors are used as on the DOT labels, there can be confusion between the two. Also, in some cases the DOT specifies a white background, which some individuals might interpret as being a lack of hazard. If some other color were selected by the label designer, then it could lead to confusion.

Another form of warning symbol that is enjoying increasingly widespread adoption in industry is the NFPA 704M system. That system is explained in detail in the NFPA book *Fire Protection Guide on Hazardous Materials*. A sample 704M label is illustrated in Figure 7. It has the

**Flammability Hazard
(Red Background)**

**Health Hazard
(Blue Background)**

**Stability Hazard
(Yellow Background)**

**Special Hazard
(White Background)**

(Water Reactivity Symbol Shown)

Figure 7. Design of the NFPA 704M hazard identification symbol.

distinct advantage of giving an indication of the severity of hazard in three different categories: flammability, dangerous reactivity or explosivity, and general health hazard.

This type of label does not give a breakdown of subclasses of hazard to the extent required by the HCS, but it does provide a good visual warning at a glance of how seriously hazardous a material is. The numerals used in each of the three hazard rating areas are 0, 1, 2, 3, and 4, with the 0 representing no significant hazard of the particular type, and the 4 representing a very serious hazard of that type. The other numbers represent intermediate degrees of hazard severity. In addition, when appropriate a symbol representing special hazard problems (water reactivity, dangerous polymerizability, oxidizer, radioactivity, etc.) is placed in the bottom section of the symbol. Detailed descriptions of the meanings of the actual ratings themselves are given in the NFPA book.

If these labels are applied at the workplace where the materials are used, they are excellent, once the workers are educated as to what they mean. It is strongly recommended that they be seriously considered for use in any kind of plant environment. However, the NFPA labels are easily confused with DOT shipping labels and are forbidden to be used in such a way that they are visible during shipment.

7   MATERIAL SAFETY DATA SHEETS

If you are a chemical manufacturer, importer, or distributor, establish a system to deliver the MSDS to each purchaser of your products. Note that MSDS must be prepared for use even with hazardous materials that are exempted from labeling requirements, such as those regulated by FDA, CPSC, FIFRA, and ATF. The delivery should be triggered automatically and could probably be handled most appropriately by your order processing department, or possibly by your billing department.

You should give careful consideration to the form you use for your MSDS. It does not have to take any particular format, according to the Hazard Communication Standard, but there are several factors involved. Some suppliers have been using the OSHA Form 20 (Figure 8) for their MSDS. It seems to carry the official sanction of OSHA, but it is inadequate under the HCS, as several items required by this Standard are not provided for on Form 20.

Some chemical companies have used a computer printout of the required information. While that practice may meet the formal requirements of the Standard, it has some problems of its own. The first, and very practical problem, is that if a manufacturer has this type of printout from several different suppliers, there will be no standardized place on all the MSDSs to find a particular type of information. This can lead to confusion, frustration, and an unwillingness to make use of the available data because to do so requires too much care—it almost amounts to pursuing a small research project each time some information is needed. That is an unreasonable burden to place on industrial workers.

Second, NO ITEMS ON THE MSDS MAY BE LEFT BLANK. If information is either not available or not applicable, in any specific category for a given material, the entry must be "n/a" rather than a blank

U.S. DEPARTMENT OF LABOR	Form Approved
Occupational Safety and Health Administration	OMB No. 44-R1387

MATERIAL SAFETY DATA SHEET

Required under USDL Safety and Health Regulations for Ship Repairing,
Shipbuilding, and Shipbreaking (29 CFR 1915, 1916, 1917)

SECTION I

MANUFACTURER'S NAME	EMERGENCY TELEPHONE NO.

ADDRESS *(Number, Street, City, State, and ZIP Code)*

CHEMICAL NAME AND SYNONYMS	TRADE NAME AND SYNONYMS

CHEMICAL FAMILY	FORMULA

SECTION II - HAZARDOUS INGREDIENTS

PAINTS, PRESERVATIVES, & SOLVENTS	%	TLV (Units)	ALLOYS AND METALLIC COATINGS	%	TLV (Units)
PIGMENTS			BASE METAL		
CATALYST			ALLOYS		
VEHICLE			METALLIC COATING		
SOLVENTS			FILLER METAL PLUS COATING OR CORE FLUX		
ADDITIVES			OTHERS		
OTHERS					

HAZARDOUS MIXTURES OF OTHER LIQUIDS, SOLIDS, OR GASES	%	TLV (Units)

SECTION III - PHYSICAL DATA

BOILING POINT (°F.)		SPECIFIC GRAVITY (H₂O=1)	
VAPOR PRESSURE (mm Hg.)		PERCENT, VOLATILE BY VOLUME (%)	
VAPOR DENSITY (AIR=1)		EVAPORATION RATE (_____ =1)	
SOLUBILITY IN WATER			
APPEARANCE AND ODOR			

SECTION IV - FIRE AND EXPLOSION HAZARD DATA

FLASH POINT (Method used)	FLAMMABLE LIMITS	Lel	Uel
EXTINGUISHING MEDIA			
SPECIAL FIRE FIGHTING PROCEDURES			
UNUSUAL FIRE AND EXPLOSION HAZARDS			

Figure 8. OSHA Form 20 (inadequate under the HCS).

SECTION V · HEALTH HAZARD DATA

THRESHOLD LIMIT VALUE

EFFECTS OF OVEREXPOSURE

EMERGENCY AND FIRST AID PROCEDURES

SECTION VI - REACTIVITY DATA

STABILITY	UNSTABLE		CONDITIONS TO AVOID
	STABLE		

INCOMPATABILITY *(Materials to avoid)*

HAZARDOUS DECOMPOSITION PRODUCTS

HAZARDOUS POLYMERIZATION	MAY OCCUR		CONDITIONS TO AVOID
	WILL NOT OCCUR		

SECTION VII · SPILL OR LEAK PROCEDURES

STEPS TO BE TAKEN IN CASE MATERIAL IS RELEASED OR SPILLED

WASTE DISPOSAL METHOD

SECTION VIII · SPECIAL PROTECTION INFORMATION

RESPIRATORY PROTECTION *(Specify type)*

VENTILATION	LOCAL EXHAUST		SPECIAL
	MECHANICAL *(General)*		OTHER

PROTECTIVE GLOVES	EYE PROTECTION

OTHER PROTECTIVE EQUIPMENT

SECTION IX · SPECIAL PRECAUTIONS

PRECAUTIONS TO BE TAKEN IN HANDLING AND STORING

OTHER PRECAUTIONS

Form OSHA-20
Rev. May 72

space. With a computer printout, it may be difficult to tell, without detailed study, whether the particular data sheet meets this requirement.

To avoid these problems, a suggested MSDS form has been designed to meet all the requirements, and it has some additional desirable features as well. A full-size blank copy of this form is provided, in a pocket inside the back cover of this book. Blanket permission is granted to copy this form and use it as often as needed. It includes a wide top margin so that you can enter your company's name and plant identification. It is suggested that chemical manufacturers and distributors use this form, or something similar. A completed sample of this form, using ethyl alcohol as an example, is shown in Figures 9 and 10.

All manufacturers might wish to enter the data from their suppliers' MSDSs on the form inside the back cover, as well as the additional information indicated, and use it as a basis for their HCS programs. The original forms from the suppliers should then be retained on file with the master copy of the written program, as documentation.

The standardized form then will be most useful to workers, as it will always have the same type of information in the same location, and the form is organized in such a way as to make it easiest to find the items most commonly sought.

As an alternative procedure, manufacturers may wish to send blank copies of this form, or an equivalent one of their own invention, to suppliers with a request that the indicated data be supplied and the form be signed and returned to the sender. Some very large corporations apparently are doing this with MSDS forms of their own design. But the Standard does not require that suppliers cooperate with such a request, and whether small firms can exert enough economic pressure to obtain their cooperation (if it is not voluntarily given) remains to be seen.

As with labels, MSDSs must be in English, though an additional copy in another language may be used also if appropriate. For example, if a large portion of your work force is made up of Spanish-speaking people whose English is poor, you may want to have an additional MSDS file just for those people.

IDENTITY OF MATERIAL

The identity of the material must be included on all MSDSs and the form of identity must make it easy to locate the sheet for any particular material. The name that is commonly used by the workers must be on the sheet as well as a chemically specific name. A specific chemical name is

MATERIAL SAFETY DATA SHEET

Section 1. Identity of Material

PRODUCT NAME OR NUMBER Ethyl Alcohol

SYNONYMS Ethanol; Grain alcohol; cologne spirits; absolute ethanol

FORMULA C_2H_5OH CAS NUMBER 64-17-5   CHEMICAL FAMILY Aliphatic alcohol

REGULATED IDENTIFICATION

DOT PROPER SHIPPING NAME Ethyl Alcohol, Ethanol

SHIPPING ID NUMBER UN 1170   NA n/a   EPA HAZARDOUS WASTE ID NUMBER n/a

HAZARDOUS INGREDIENTS	%	CAS NUMBER
Ethyl Alcohol	100	64-17-5

Section 2. Hazard Specifications

KNOWN HAZARDS UNDER 29 CFR 1910.1200

TLV = 1000   ppm. 1900   mg/m³
PEL = 1000   ppm. 1900   mg/m³

	YES	NO		YES	NO
COMBUSTIBLE LIQUID	X		SKIN HAZARD	X	
FLAMMABLE MATERIAL	X		EYE HAZARD	X	
PYROPHORIC MATERIAL		X	TOXIC AGENT		X
EXPLOSIVE MATERIAL		X	HIGHLY TOXIC AGENT		X
UNSTABLE MATERIAL		X	SENSITIZER		X
WATER REACTIVE MATERIAL		X	CARCINOGEN	X	
OXIDIZER		X	REPRODUCTIVE TOXIN		X
ORGANIC PEROXIDE		X	BLOOD TOXIN		X
CORROSIVE MATERIAL		X	NERVOUS SYSTEM TOXIN	X	
COMPRESSED GAS		X	LUNG TOXIN		X
IRRITANT	X		LIVER TOXIN	X	
			KIDNEY TOXIN	X	

NFPA HAZARD SIGNAL

HEALTH 0   FLAMMABILITY 3

STABILITY 0   SPECIAL n/a

DOT HAZARD CLASS

Flammable Liquid

EPA HAZARD WASTE CLASS

Ignitable Waste

Section 3. Safe Usage Data

PROTECTIVE EQUIPMENT TYPES

EYES Chemical splash goggles; Face shield for open large volumes

RESPIRATORY Air supply mask when cleaning process equip. or lg. spills

GLOVES Rubber or neoprene

OTHER Rubber or vinyl apron, rubber boots for cleanup operations

VENTILATION

GENERAL MECHANICAL Normally suitable with floor-level exhaust

LOCAL EXHAUST When handling open vessels, particularly if heated

PRECAUTIONS

HANDLING & STORAGE Store in cool place, away from ignition sources, oxidizers, mineral acids, active metals; use closed safety cans/grounded drums.

OTHER Avoid swallowing or contact with eyes or skin.

Figure 9. Material safety data sheet for ethyl alcohol, side 1.

Section 4. Emergency Response Data

FIRE	EXTINGUISHING MEDIA Dry chemical, "alcohol" foam, CO$_2$; fog for large fires
	SPECIAL PROCEDURES Use water to cool containers exposed to heat of fire.
	UNUSUAL HAZARDS Large tanks BLEVE (Boiling Liquid Expanding Vapor Explosi⟩
EXPOSURE	FIRST AID MEASURES Fresh air, artificial respiration or oxygen if needed. Irrigate eyes with water; wash skin with soap and water.
SPILLS RQ = n/a	STEPS TO BE TAKEN Shut off ignition source; stop leak if possible; water spray to reduce vapors; use absorbent material; dike large spills
	WASTE DISPOSAL METHOD incinerate; sewer if local conditions allow.

Section 5. Physical Hazard Data

FLAMMABILITY	LFL = 3.3 %		FLASH POINT 55 °F 13 °C	
	UFL = 19 %		METHOD USED closed cup	
STABILITY	STABLE X	CONDITIONS TO AVOID n/a		
	UNSTABLE	HAZARDOUS DECOMP PDTS n/a		
HAZARDOUS POLYMERIZATION	MAY OCCUR	CONDITIONS TO AVOID		
	WILL NOT OCCUR X	n/a		
INCOMPATIBILITY	MATERIALS TO AVOID Mineral acids, oxidizers, active metals, acid anhydrides, acid chlorides, organic peroxides			

Section 6. Health Hazard Data

EFFECTS OF EXPOSURE Oral: nausea, vomiting, flushing, drowsiness, impaired perceptio
Vapor: immediate stinging and burning of eyes, irritation of upper respir.
tract, incoordination, drowsiness, narcosis, headaches, sensation of heat,
~~eye tension, fatigue, stupor, great need for sleep.~~

EMERGENCY TREATMENT Artificial respiration or oxygen if needed.
If swallowed, gastric lavage followed by saline catharsis.

Section 7. Physical and Chemical Properties

BOILING PT = 173.3 °F 78.5 °C	VAPOR DENSITY (AIR 1) 1.59	VOLATILE COMPONENTS 100 %
VAPOR PRESS = 43 mmHg @20°C xx	pH n/a	Density = 0.789 g/cc
SOLUBILITY IN H$_2$O 100 %	WILL DISSOLVE IN most organic solvents	EVAPORATION RATE (=1) n/a
APPEARANCE Clear, colorless, mobile liquid		IS MATERIAL PASTE POWDER
ODOR Pleasant odor, burning taste		SOLID (LIQUID) GAS

Section 8. Manufacturer or Supplier Data

FIRM'S NAME & MAILING ADDRESS John Doe Chemical Company 1000 North Main Street Anywhere, U.S.A.	NAME (PRINT) John Q. Doe
	SIGNATURE John Q. Doe
	TITLE President
	DATE March 1, 1985
	EMERGENCY TELEPHONE NO XXX-XXX-XXXX

Figure 10. Material safety data sheet for ethyl alcohol, side 2.

one that will permit any qualified chemist to identify the structure of the compound(s) present to enable further searching of the literature for desired information. This identity will usually be a systematic scientific name, often accompanied by its unique Chemical Abstracts Service (CAS) registry number.

Mixtures

If the hazardous material is a mixture that has been tested for hazards, the chemical name(s) of the substance(s) which contribute those known hazards to the mixture must be given, as well as the common name of the mixture itself, if it has one. If the hazardous material is a mixture that has not been tested as a whole for hazards, the ingredients that contribute to the actual or presumed hazards of the mixture must be listed, but the actual composition need not be.

Trade Secrets

If the composition of the hazardous mixture is a trade secret, the chemical identities of the ingredients need not be disclosed on the MSDS, but the hazards they present must be specified as well as appropriate protective or precautionary measures to be used with the material. More specific data about the composition of trade secret mixtures can be obtained by qualified health professionals or by OSHA under appropriate conditions and for certain types of reasons, such as a need for monitoring workplace air or for medical surveillance of exposed employees.

CONTROL OF HAZARDS

Hazard Specifications

TLVs, or OSHA permissible exposure limits (PELs), or both, must be listed where they have been determined. However, remember that these values have not been assigned for the vast majority of hazardous materials — only those listed in Appendix 3.

Safe Usage Data

Generally applicable control and monitoring methods as well as general precautions for safe use are to be given on the MSDS also. This information must include appropriate measures to be taken during repair and maintenance of contaminated equipment.

Emergency Response Data

Emergency and first aid procedures that are appropriate for workers exposed to the material must be included. Applicable control and monitoring methods to be used during cleanup of spills and leaks must also be included in the information on the MSDS.

If the material has a "Reportable Quantity" (RQ) or RCRA Hazardous Waste Identification Number assigned by EPA, these might well be included on the MSDS also, though they are not required by OSHA.

CHARACTERISTICS OF MATERIAL

Physical Hazard Data

The physical hazards of the material must be indicated, including potential for fire, explosion, and reactivity.

Health Hazard Data

The health hazards of the material must also be indicated, including signs and symptoms of exposure as well as any medical conditions known to be aggravated by exposure to the particular material. Along with the health hazards, the principal routes of exposure must be given (e.g., skin, eyes, GI tract, respiratory system). *Indication must also be made as to whether the compound is a listed carcinogen.*

Physical and Chemical Properties

The MSDS must include physical and chemical characteristics of the hazardous chemical such as density relative to water, density of gas or vapor relative to air, boiling point, melting point, flash point, flammability range and vapor pressure at one or more temperatures.

SUPPLIER OR MANUFACTURER DATA

An essential part of the MSDS is the date of its preparation and the name, address and telephone number of a responsible party who can provide additional information if necessary.

8 WRITTEN HAZARD COMMUNICATION PROGRAM

Your written hazard communication program must include: (1) a list of hazardous materials by plant area; (2) the material safety data sheets, and descriptions of how they are prepared and how they are made available to employees; (3) a description of how labels and other forms of warning are prepared and used; and (4) a description of the training and information procedures used for employees and others.

The written program does not have to be available to all employees at all times, but upon request it must be made available to them or their designated representatives or to OSHA. The lists of hazardous materials and the MSDSs do have to be available at all times, though. Copies of the written program should be kept in the safety department and in the plant manager's office, as well as in any other locations thought desirable in line with company organization and policy.

THE HAZARDOUS MATERIALS FILE

Preparation of the List

As you prepare your inventory of hazardous materials, arrange the list alphabetically. Be sure that the name used by the plant workers is included on the list, as well as the name on the label and any other names included on the MSDS or the label. These should be cross-referenced to the principal name on the MSDS, so that it can be found as quickly as possible.

Often the name used by plant workers is a convenient one that has no obvious connection to the name on the MSDS, so cross-referencing is necessary. Following are a few examples of the types of nicknames that are sometimes used by plant workers when speaking of chemicals they use:

- "Caustic" refers to sodium hydroxide, also known as caustic soda.
- "Monomer" refers to styrene monomer (or vinyl chloride monomer, or methyl methacrylate monomer). There are many different monomers, but in a particular plant the term may be used for a specific compound and should be referenced in that way on your hazardous materials list.
- "Plasticizer" refers to di-2-ethylhexyl phthalate.

Once you have completed your list with cross-references, prepare a sublist for each area or department if you have a large operation. The complete list must be kept current in the written program. It should include notations as to which sublists contain each substance, and in which departments or areas each material is located.

This list is for those hazardous materials known to be present. If a reasonable effort is made to determine whether something is hazardous and no such properties are found, it isn't necessary to undertake a major research project to find some. However, the effort used must be reasonable and significant — not just a cursory inquiry — and it must be documented.

Documentation of Procedure

The supplier of a hazardous material is legally responsible for identifying the hazards present and for supplying a properly completed MSDS. Manufacturers who buy and use hazardous materials are responsible for attempting to obtain the MSDS for them. If you do not receive an MSDS for a particular substance that you suspect might be hazardous, write a letter to your vendor requesting one.

If you do not receive a response to your request within a reasonable time, write a second letter requesting that you be supplied either an MSDS or a disclaimer that the material is not hazardous under the Standard. Keep copies of these letters with your master hazardous materials list. If you receive neither an MSDS nor a disclaimer, copies of the two letters will document the fact that you were diligent in your attempt to learn whether the material is hazardous.

Also, a statement must be included describing how the hazards were determined for the listed materials. If the information supplied by the vendors was relied upon, a statement to that effect is needed. If, however, the employer or some other person made the determination of hazards, then the criteria used and the reference sources consulted need to be listed. This kind of statement will indicate to any appropriate person whether a reasonable and significant effort was made to identify and characterize all the hazards involved.

Maintenance of Material Safety Data Sheets

Even if you obtain MSDSs from vendors, you may wish to do as some companies have already done—prepare your own MSDSs (or contract the job to a consulting firm), using those supplied by vendors as a starting point. An appropriate form to use is available in Appendix 2 (and inside the back cover), and its use is described in Chapter 7.

On a regular, systematic basis you should prepare new sheets as needed and review existing ones. Use the emergency telephone number on the MSDS for additional information about the material, if you feel it is needed for any reason. If you learn about any hazard information, or safe usage methods, that are not already stated on the MSDS for a particular material, you are required to add that information to the MSDS within 90 days. If you are not a chemical manufacturer or distributor, you also have a moral obligation to report such information to the manufacturer who prepared the original MSDS.

MATERIALS MANAGEMENT

Purchasing

Involve the purchasing department in your materials management program. They should automatically request a copy, either new or updated if appropriate, as a part of each order for materials. This might involve using a rubber stamp or printed memo, with a notation of the date of preparation of the most recent version of the MSDS you have received from that vendor. Immediately on receipt, these should be forwarded to the custodian of the MSDS and written program files. A policy should be established to see that all materials purchased on petty cash, as well as sales samples of materials, also enter the system.

Storage and Inventory

Track all chemicals from their initial introduction into the workplace, so that the location of each material is known at all times. Its actual location must always correspond to the information on the hazardous materials list in the written program.

Be sure that all containers are accurately labeled with their current contents. If the supplier hasn't done so to your satisfaction, do it yourself or have someone in your organization do it on a routine basis.

Disposal and Emergency Procedures

Your written program must contain an outline of emergency procedures. This should include a policy statement regarding emergency treatment procedures for personnel who might be accidentally exposed to hazardous materials above the permitted level. You should always plan to send the appropriate MSDSs to the hospital or other treatment facility with workers who are exposed to chemicals. A statement to this effect needs to be included in your written plan.

The plan should also include a system to accumulate statistics on exposures, and desirably on "near misses" as well. Such recordkeeping often is required by regulatory agencies anyway, and it should be included in this written plan. Based on the data accumulated to document experience with the program, your system and procedures might be made more effective.

Put your emergency procedures into writing. This should explain how the firm and each area within it will handle fires, floods, or explosions. Such emergencies, since they can cause a release of a hazardous substance into the environment, are covered by the Standard.

The emergency procedures should also include a description of how leaks and spills will be handled. The actual cleanup and disposal procedures may come under EPA's jurisdiction rather than OSHA's. It is recommended, though, that the EPA-required documentation be included as part of your written program under the HCS, for your own convenience and efficiency. This will include information on reportable quantities, required reporting, necessary telephone numbers, and even the entire RCRA-required contingency plan.

TRAINING

Be sure to document your training of personnel. It is also recommended that your EPA-required training of personnel who handle hazardous waste be included here, as much of it overlaps the HCS-required training.

Employee Training

A description of the methods used to inform and train the employees under the provisions of the Standard must be included. This will include not only the training for routine operations but also for nonroutine cleaning of equipment, and cleanup of spills and leaks.

The hazard information is communicated to employees in several ways, some of which are covered in detail elsewhere and will merely be mentioned here. The methods include package labels, material safety data sheets, a written hazard communication program, and specific employee training. The methods used to inform employees of the hazards associated with chemicals contained in unlabeled pipes in their work areas must be included.

Maintenance personnel, security personnel, delivery crews, messengers, and design engineers, for example, must be informed about the hazards in the various areas which they may visit in the course of their duties. The procedures used to inform these and any other occasionally exposed employees must be included.

Finally you must include information about how you train employees who seldom visit production departments. You may restrict such visits to minimize liability, or you may give all employees some abbreviated form of the training, or you may train selectively. But again, what you do must be stated in your written program.

Informing Non-Employees

Prepare a policy on how the training and notification of contractors and their employees working in the plant will be handled. Written agreements should be prepared for repeat contractors such as cleaning or maintenance suppliers.

You may want to brief the contractor's foreman or superintendant on the hazards, furnishing him or her a copy of the written program, and advising that all contractor's personnel be trained as appropriate for their potential exposure. Whether this is the approach used, or something more elaborate, it must be detailed in the training section of the written program.

Invite the local fire department to survey the storage and use of chemicals in the plant, particularly if significant quantities are involved. Also notify the local medical community that emergency exposure information is available. A statement should be included in your written program to indicate that these notifications have been, or will be, made.

Documentation

All training and information sessions of any kind need to be documented as to subjects covered, times, dates, instructors and/or packaged programs used, and names of employees attending.

9   EMPLOYEE TRAINING

OSHA considers training to be one of "three vital components," along with labels and material safety data sheets, in a comprehensive hazard communication program. The success of an employee training program will in turn depend to a large extent on the quality of relations between employer and employee. OSHA suggests that training programs will be more effective if employees are allowed to assist in designing them. While this is probably not practical in all situations, some form of employee feedback should be encouraged so that the success of the program can be monitored.

However you handle your training, don't forget to include the following items in your written hazard communication program: goals; objectives; types of training sessions used; quizzes used; quiz results; dates and times and names of those attending training sessions.

INFORMATION ABOUT THE STANDARD

The OSHA Hazard Communication Standard requires that all employees must be told about the main features of the Standard: labels, MSDSs, written program, lists of hazardous materials, and required training. These features can be summarized without much detail other than what is needed to answer questions. It would be appropriate to include the full text of the Standard in the written program so that employees may refer to it if they wish. They must be told the location of the written program and that it is available to them or to their designated representatives upon request.

They must also be told about the list of hazardous materials in the workplace, how to use it, where to find it, and that it is available for inspection at any time during working hours. They must also be told where the material safety data sheets are kept, and that these too are available for inspection at any time during working hours. It is suggested that a summary of these provisions be available at all times on suitably located posters in the plant.

SUBJECT OF TRAINING

All employees, old as well as new, must be told about the hazards posed by all the materials they work with that are covered under the Standard. They must be told how to detect the presence of the materials, how to use personal protective equipment properly, what emergency procedures to use in case of leaks and spills, and what procedures are to be used in nonroutine tasks such as maintenance and cleaning of contaminated equipment. This training must be updated whenever a new hazardous material is introduced into the workplace, and critical aspects of the training should be repeated periodically even if no new materials are introduced.

Recognition of Hazards

Employees must be told about the various forms of identity (synonyms) for the material. They may be accustomed to talking about a particular material with a common name that has little resemblance to its scientific name or proper shipping name. But they must be told about the various names and how to use the cross-indexed list of hazardous materials to find the MSDS for any material for which they want the information.

Along with the name identity, they must be told how to recognize the material if it should be released in the workplace. This can include such things as its color, its state (solid, liquid, or gas), its general appearance and odor (if any), and where it is used in the process. Any monitoring instruments that are normally used or that are available for use as needed should be described. Those who actually use such monitoring instruments need to be instructed in their proper use.

Understanding Hazards

All employees also must be told about the hazards themselves (what they are, and what they mean in terms of recognizable phenomena or symptoms) as well as the risks accompanying each hazard. The risk instruction will include some discussion of how serious the effect is that occurs if the hazard actually does result in harm to health or property. It should also discuss how easily and how likely these things are to happen.

This is the most difficult part of any safety instruction program. It is very easy for employees to overreact to a minimal hazard and become paranoid. It is even easier for foremen, supervisors, and long-time employees to ignore hazards, because frequently they have been around such materials for many years without ever seeing a problem. This does not mean that a hazard does not exist, though, and the situation must be discussed openly, frankly, and honestly.

Protection Against Hazards

A vital part of the instruction about risks and hazards is the discussion of precautionary procedures, equipment, and control measures that are designed to reduce the risk of harm from a particular hazard. This information should be stressed as an important aspect of reducing both the probability of exposure and the severity of harm if exposure should occur.

Finally, several nonroutine aspects of the hazards of any particular material need to be discussed with employees. If they are involved in cleanup of contaminated equipment, either on a routine periodic basis or when the process is shut down for a period of time, they need to know about the special protective equipment and measures to be used, which usually are more stringent than during normal operations. Similar training is needed for procedures used in the emergency cleanup of spills and leaks. This is also the point to introduce instruction about personnel evacuation procedures.

Appropriate first aid procedures need to be discussed, and sometimes even practiced. Another subject related to emergencies is that of fire control — whether to use extinguishers, what kind, and how, and at what stage to call the professionals and evacuate the area.

Finally, routine medical surveillance procedures, if used, should be explained. The reasons for using such procedures should also be carefully explained. Frequently employees consider medical surveillance to be harassment without recognizing that it is designed to protect them by monitoring their systems for negligible effects that could become major problems if not detected and corrected at an early stage.

Availability of Hazard Information

In addition to the general provisions of the Standard, employees must be told specifically where they can find hazard information when they want it. This is primarily a matter of telling them where to look for information on the labels, where to find the written program, what it includes, how to use the hazardous materials list, and how to read and understand the MSDS.

EXECUTION OF TRAINING

Goals and Objectives

The starting point for any formal training program is to determine its goals and objectives. Under the requirements of this Standard, the primary goals are to impart to the workers an understanding of: (1) the hazards presented by the materials in the workplace; (2) the risks connected with the presence of those hazards; and (3) the implications of those risks for precautions and emergency response.

Objectives are specific, single-concept statements of what is to be accomplished by the training. Some training programs may have dozens or even hundreds of individual objectives. An objective should state precisely what is to be learned, in terms of definite recognizable or testable features.

A possible set of objectives is as follows:
"Upon completion of the training, for each hazardous material in the work area, each worker will be able to

- know the chemical identity as well as the common name;
- know where it is used in his or her area of the plant;
- know how to identify it by odor and appearance when it is not mixed with other substances;
- know what its physical hazards are;

- know how to deal with an accidental fire in which it is involved;
- know what its acute health hazards are;
- know the symptoms to be expected for the acute health hazards;
- know what first aid steps to use for a worker who has been exposed to it and is suffering its acute symptoms;
- know what steps to take in the event a quantity of it is accidentally spilled;
- know what its chronic health hazards are;
- know what protective equipment to wear to minimize exposure;
- know the proper way to wear the protective equipment;
- know where to find any additional information needed about the hazardous properties of the material."

In addition to these, there should be other objectives that are not specific to materials. These might include: the location of the written program; the location of the list of hazardous materials; the location of the MSDS; how to use the list to find the appropriate MSDS; plant evacuation procedures; and other emergency procedures.

Once all the objectives for the complete training program have been written, they should become part of the written hazard communication program. All training under the Standard should revolve about those objectives: individual orientation sessions; periodic safety training meetings; and evaluation of material learned in the sessions or meetings.

Types of Training

When the objectives have been established, one of the first steps is to do a "walk-through" orientation of all employees who have not already been trained in these matters. This orientation is to show employees what hazardous materials are used in the plant, and where. At this time, material identification and the location of labels or batch tickets can be discussed. This should usually be one of the first steps in the training of a new employee.

Following the walk-through, the other aspects of the objectives that deal with the materials in the area should be covered in a general safety meeting for the employees involved. Appropriate portions of this training need to be repeated for all employees whenever new hazardous materials are introduced into the workplace.

At the end of each session, it is advisable to give trainees a quiz over the material covered. Quizzes should be graded and problem areas discussed with the individuals. Then the quizzes, or at least a record of scores together with dates and times involved in training, should go into an appropriate file as evidence that the required training was given. This can be an important part of the employee feedback mentioned in the first paragraph of this chapter. The exact nature and use of the quizzes is a matter for local determination.

Some unions may object to giving quizzes. However, written safety exams have long been a part of the industrial scene for various types of work, such as operation of forklift trucks, and chemical hazards would seem to merit serious consideration in this respect also. If objections are raised, it may be necessary to negotiate such testing policies and procedures into the next contract.

Safety training sessions should be held on a regular, periodic basis, preferably monthly. The Standard represents a complex subject. Depending on the nature and number of hazardous materials in your workplace, it may not be learned well on the first attempt, and portions of it (particularly emergency response and first aid) that are not used often are easily forgotten. Employees can be "turned off" by safety meetings that seem to be a pointless waste of time. But if their quiz scores show that their knowledge is inadequate, they may recognize the importance of actively participating in safety instruction.

These training sessions may take any form that will accomplish the goals and objectives. Some "hands-on" training is desirable, such as actual practice at putting on a self-contained breathing apparatus for emergency response. One only has to do this once to be convinced that it is not something that comes naturally, but has to be learned. Another example is training in the recognition of materials by odor and appearance. Small containers of materials used in the plant area can be brought in and the workers asked to identify each. CAUTION: Smelling some of these substances can be very dangerous. It must be done properly, and particularly harmful materials should be diluted enough to prevent a dangerous dosage by careless sniffing.

Training aids are available to help with many aspects of this training. Movies, tape/slide programs, slides with narrative scripts, posters, and other aids are available from safety supply companies, national, local, or regional safety councils, manufacturers of safety equipment, and other sources. Some of these are not as good as others, but nearly all can be useful within their intended range of purposes.

Be sure that the training includes all the nonroutine items as well as the routine. Instruction in emergency response, spill cleanup, and cleaning of contaminated equipment must be provided. The training given maintenance and plant security personnel may be much different than that given production workers, or all may be included in the same sessions, depending on your individual situation.

Documentation

The results of quizzes after each training session will often tell you what topics need to be covered again soon, and what topics seem to have been learned well enough that only occasional reminders will be needed. For material on which quiz scores were somewhere between these extremes, occasional reviews are appropriate until everyone is well trained.

All training and information sessions of any kind need to be documented as to subjects covered, times, dates, instructors and/or packaged programs used, and names of employees attending. An up-to-date summary of this information should also be maintained in each employee's personnel file for all training received.

10   CONSEQUENCES

Any new government requirements can cause problems among those who are regulated, however well-intentioned those requirements might be. In the case of the Hazard Communication Standard, there is no assurance that significant problems will in fact appear, other than the task of meeting the requirements. But based on experience with other regulations having some similar features, a few troublesome areas might be expected, though the problems should not be crippling.

The comments offered in this chapter are based mainly on observations and anecdotal evidence, so it is uncertain how accurate the predictions will be. Probably there is no way to be sure of the ultimate outcome in these matters in advance.

On the average, the overall effect is more likely to be positive than negative. However, there still may be a negative effect in some situations. How the plant management personnel handle particular situations will often have more to do with the overall consequences of compliance than will the provisions of the Standard itself.

In any case, if such problems do arise, many of them undoubtedly will be temporary results of the change rather than permanent effects of the Standard itself. Part of the problem is the generally bad publicity, often ill-informed, given to all sorts of problems related to hazardous materials in recent years. It may even be that this fact will mitigate the problems experienced by individual plants somewhat. That is, if the public sees that something positive is being done to bring things under control, that fact may offset some of the concerns about individual materials.

POTENTIAL PROBLEMS

Chemical Suppliers

Generally, most manufacturers, importers, and distributors of chemical products probably will make a good faith effort to meet the spirit as well as the letter of this Standard. It may be, though, that some chemical suppliers will be reluctant to furnish the required information.

Some may not believe that their products could be hazardous and will simply not do an adequate job of characterizing them. If you have a supplier who doesn't seem to want to cooperate by furnishing proper labels and MSDSs or a disclaimer, you have at least three alternative courses of action.

One possible course of action is simply to assume that once you have made a good faith effort to obtain the information, you have discharged your responsibility in this respect.

Another course is to seek another supplier who might cooperate better. If a particular product is proprietary and its composition is a trade secret, then you can either accept the situation or try to find another product that will do the same job.

Still a third course of action is to evaluate the hazards and prepare your own MSDS for the material. If material hazards are indeed characterized by you, that fact should be communicated to the vendor. If your firm does not have the in-house expertise needed to make such an evaluation, you may contract with a knowledgeable consultant to do the job for you.

Employees

A second area of possible problems is with your employees, and several types of problems might be encountered.

Paranoia

Some employees may overreact to the disclosure of hazards and effectively refuse to work with such materials. One response to this situation is to try to persuade such individuals that the danger is less than they fear, provided they follow the precautions that are recommended for each material. Another response is to let the employee leave the firm. If he or she is afraid of the job conditions to that extent, then continued effective work within the situation might not be possible anyway.

If he or she refuses to work under such conditions but refuses to quit the job, then you have a problem that must be dealt with by personnel experts rather than by chemists or industrial hygienists. In any case this is a difficult problem that may not occur often, but it is more likely if training is inadequate, by poorly informed instructors, than if it is well done.

A related problem is that sometimes it may be difficult to hire secretarial and clerical personnel to work in an office where such hazards are known or rumored to exist in an adjacent plant. Education is probably the only appropriate answer to this problem. If the company's safety record is a good one, the task should be somewhat easier. One might simply not worry about such people as long as enough competent staff can be hired, but that wouldn't help the company's image.

Apathy

Another problem, that is almost the opposite of the first, is worker apathy. Some workers don't pay attention to safety instruction and therefore don't learn the material as well as they should. In such cases, be sure to document the instruction received and then repeat and review those areas of instruction that seem especially weak. Seek to impress on employees that learning this material is in their own self interest as well as being a very important part of their overall job responsibilities.

If a few employees become a particular problem in this respect, then you again have a personnel policy problem to deal with, just as with any other type of situation in which an employee does not discharge his or her duties properly.

Hypochondria

An employee-related problem that some managers fear most about this Standard is that it might increase the number of employees who "call in sick." Thus, if employees are told that overexposure to vapors of a certain material can cause headaches or nausea, some may use that fact as an excuse to collect sick leave pay, or they may become honestly convinced that they suffer the symptoms described. Indeed, this may happen in some cases, particularly if labor relations are poor, but the frequency of such incidents probably will not vary much from what it has been all along.

A few appropriate responses to such apparent cases can be suggested. First, a clinical test may sometimes be indicated. That is, for some workplace contaminants, urine or blood tests can be run to detect and measure the presence of significant amounts of the substance in a person's body. At the time of this writing, there are only a few such authenticated tests available, but they deal with some of the more common hazardous materials, and tests for other materials are being developed all the time.

Sometimes such a complaining worker can be transferred to another location in the plant where exposure to the problem material can be discontinued. Combining this action with records detailing numbers and types of complaints received from workers in different areas of the plant can help to understand the true nature of the problem. It may expose hypochondriacs and malingerers, or it may reveal actual problems, for example with ventilation, that had not been fully recognized previously.

Plant Neighbors

Similar to the reluctance of office personnel to work near "chemicals" is the increasingly militant resistance of citizens to the presence of presumed or actual hazardous operations near their homes. They cannot believe that the hazards have only low risk for them, and at times it seems that no amount of reassurance will help. This, of course, is a public relations problem, and not a simple one.

It is possible that the presence of this Standard will make the problem worse by calling attention to the hazards. But it also may be that the amount of disclosure provided will help the situation when better understanding is achieved. Only time will tell, and in fact the two extremes may exist at the same time at different locations.

Being aware that this type of problem can arise will allow you to alert your public relations people. They can then prepare to meet the problem head on if it does indeed arise. If they are unprepared for the problem they may be taken by surprise, with unhappy consequences.

OSHA Inspectors

Some employers seem worried that they will have frequent OSHA inspections as a result of this Standard. OSHA doesn't have, nor will it soon have, enough inspectors to harass very many people, even if they were inclined to do so.

If and when you do have a visit from an OSHA inspector for any purpose at all, he or she will likely ask to see your written hazard communication program, and if it seems to be in good order, you should have no problems with it. Of course, if someone files a complaint because they believe you are not adhering to the Standard properly, then you will receive closer scrutiny. Simply complying with the Standard, though, certainly will not be an invitation for excessive inspections.

Litigation

Finally, there is the question as to whether the Standard will affect the likelihood of lawsuits, and if so, how? If you are in reasonable compliance, you may actually be less likely to attract suits for negligence than under previously existing conditions where employees have not been informed about materials they work with. Just because an employee will know more about potential harm from particular substances in the workplace, that does not seem likely to increase the chances of a suit in a case of illness years later. But no one can predict such things with any degree of certainty.

Actually, some of the liability suits that have been filed in recent years probably would not have occurred if the employees had been informed of the kinds of things that this Standard requires. That is, sometimes a former employee "presumes" that his health problems were caused by something he had been exposed to in the workplace when in fact the particular kind of problem is not known to be associated with the particular chemical. If full disclosure had been made much earlier, it is possible some such suits would never have been filed.

POTENTIAL ADVANTAGES

In plants where the Hazard Communications Standard is handled well, there are several aspects of operations that might well be improved as a result.

Reduction of Illness and Injuries

When employees know of the potential hazards and the risks involved, they may be more careful of how they handle such materials. This in turn can lead to less frequent and less serious accidental spills, if these have been a problem in the past. Also, awareness of the type of problems for which the Standard was designed should encourage employees to use protective equipment and procedures better. It might also reduce the tendency for horseplay among those who may be so inclined. All these factors should lead to fewer accidents and less time lost, as well as generally better productivity.

As a result of having fewer and less serious injuries and illnesses, plant first aid costs might be reduced, and workers' compensation and health insurance claims could even decline, thereby perhaps lowering premiums the company pays. These are of course speculative, but they are not unreasonable expectations and they could possibly be significant benefits of compliance.

Employee Morale

If developments occur as suggested in the above section, worker morale could improve. The usual consequence of this is a decreased turnover rate in the work force, as well as fewer labor relations problems. The net savings in overhead costs can be significant.

System Improvement

One very realistic beneficial prospect of this Standard is a result of not just the workers but also of management at all levels becoming increasingly aware of the nature of material hazards. As a result, sometimes changes in equipment or procedures are motivated, resulting in fewer spills and accidents. This in turn means less downtime, less expense of emergency response, and less worker lost time—in short, improved productivity.

Uniform Minimum Standards

Although new federal regulations are frequently viewed as unwanted intrusions by "Big Brother," the Hazard Communication Standard should provide some real benefits by virtue of being primarily a single standard applied uniformly. Fewer states should be inclined to impose their own special standards, and those who decide to do so will have to secure the approval of the Secretary of Labor. Not only will firms that have plants in several different states benefit from more uniform standards, but also "downstream" employers will be able to depend on receiving MSDSs and labels for chemicals they purchase from out-of-state suppliers.

Public Image

Finally, if your program is well implemented, reduced fear of the unknown among employees and neighbors could even lead to an improved relationship with the nearby community. In fact, some major chemical companies already are voluntarily disclosing material hazard information to the communities in which their facilities are located, just for this reason. This is the "flip side" of the potential problem mentioned previously in which neighbors hear about the hazards and cannot believe that they are less serious than imagined.

SELECTED REFERENCES

Anderson, K., and R. Scott, *Fundamentals of Industrial Toxicology* (Ann Arbor, MI: Ann Arbor Science Publishers, Inc., 1981)

Braker, W., and A. L. Mossman, *Matheson Gas Data Book,* 5th ed. (East Rutherford, NJ: Matheson Gas Products, 1971)

Braker, W., A. L. Mossman and D. Siegel, *Effects of Exposure to Toxic Gases—First Aid and Medical Treatment* (Lyndhurst, NJ: Matheson, 1977)

Bretherick, L., *Handbook of Reactive Chemical Hazards* (Cleveland, OH: CRC Press, Inc., 1975)

Browning, R. L., *The Loss Rate Concept in Safety Engineering* (New York: Marcel Dekker, Inc., 1980)

Clayton, G. D., and F. E. Clayton, Eds., *Patty's Industrial Hygiene and Toxicology, 3rd Rev. Ed., Vol. I, General Practices* (New York: John Wiley & Sons, 1978)

Clayton, G. D., and F. E. Clayton, Eds., *Patty's Industrial Hygiene and Toxicology, 3rd Rev. Ed., Vol. II, Toxicology* (New York: John Wiley & Sons, 1982)

Cralley, L. J., and L. V. Cralley, Eds., *Patty's Industrial Hygiene and Toxicology, 3rd Rev. Ed., Vol. III, Theory and Rationale of Industrial Hygiene Practice* (New York: John Wiley & Sons, 1978)

Documentation of the Threshold Limit Values, 4th ed., (Cincinnati, OH: ACGIH, 1980)

Encyclopedia of Chemical Technology, 12 vols. (New York: Wiley-Interscience, 1978-80)

Fawcett, H. H., and W. S. Wood, *Safety and Accident Prevention in Chemical Operations* (New York: Wiley-Interscience, 1965)

Fire Protection Guide on Hazardous Materials, 7th ed. (Boston, MA: National Fire Protection Association, 1978)

Hazard Communication, OSHA, 29 CFR 1910.1200

Hazardous Materials: Emergency Response Guidebook (Washington, DC: U.S. Department of Transportation, Materials Transport Bureau)

Lowrance, W. W., *Of Acceptable Risk: Science and the Determination of Safety* (Los Altos, CA: William Kaufmann, Inc., 1976)

Meidl, J. H., *Flammable Hazardous Materials,* 2nd Ed. (New York: Macmillan, 1978)

Meyer, E., *Chemistry of Hazardous Materials* (Englewood Cliffs, NJ: Prentice-Hall, 1977)

Muir, G. D., *Hazards in the Chemical Laboratory* (London: the Chemical Society, 1977)

Occupational Safety and Health Act, 29 USC 651-78

L. Parmeggiani, Ed., *Encyclopedia of Occupational Health and Safety* (Geneva: International Labor Office, 1983)

Prudent Practices for Handling Hazardous Chemicals in Laboratories, National Research Council (Washington, DC: National Academy Press, 1981)

Registry of Toxic Effects of Chemical Substances (Rockville, MD: U.S. Department of Health and Human Services, Public Health Service, NIOSH)

Rodricks, J. V., and R. G. Tardiff, Eds., *Assessment and Management of Chemical Risks* (Washington, DC: American Chemical Society, 1984)

Safe Handling of Chemical Carcinogens, Mutagens, Teratogens, and Highly Toxic Substances (Woburn, MA: Butterworths, 1980)

Sax, N. I., *Cancer Causing Chemicals* (New York: Van Nostrand Reinhold Co., 1981)

Sax, N. I., and B. Feiner, *Dangerous Properties of Industrial Materials,* 6th ed. (New York: Van Nostrand Reinhold Co., 1984)

Sittig, M., *Handbook of Toxic and Hazardous Chemicals* (Park Ridge, NJ: Noyes Publications, 1981)

Steere, N. V., Ed., *Handbook of Laboratory Safety,* 2nd ed. (Cleveland, OH: CRC Press, Inc., 1971)

Threshold Limit Values for Chemical Substances and Physical Agents in the Work Environment (Cincinnati, OH, ACGIH, 1984 et seq)

Toxic and Hazardous Industrial Chemicals Safety Manual, (Tokyo, Japan: The International Technical Information Institute, 1977)

Toxic and Hazardous Substances, OSHA, 29 CFR 1910, Subpart Z

Training Guidelines, OSHA, 48 FR 39317-23, August 30, 1983

Tuve, R. L., *Principles of Fire Protection Chemistry* (Boston, MA: National Fire Protection Association, 1976)

Verschueren, K., *Handbook of Environmental Data on Organic Chemicals* (New York: Van Nostrand Reinhold Co., 1977)

Weinstein, A. S., A. D. Twerski, H. R. Piehler and W. A. Donaher, *Products Liability and the Reasonably Safe Product* (New York: John Wiley & Sons, 1978)

Windholz, M., S. Budavari, L. Y. Stroumtsos and M. N. Fertig, Eds., *The Merck Index: An Encyclopedia of Chemicals and Drugs* (Rahway, NJ: Merck & Co. Inc., 1976)

APPENDICES

APPENDIX 1
TEXT OF THE OSHA HAZARD COMMUNICATION STANDARD

In this appendix, the full text of the Standard (29 CFR 1910.1200) is included for reference. Finding needed information in such official documents can sometimes be a difficult and confusing task, even for those who are already familiar with the material. The following guide to the contents, keyed to the sections and subsections within the Standard, is offered to make the task somewhat easier.

GUIDE TO THE STANDARD

(a) Purpose
   (1) Ensure evaluation and communication of hazards
   (2) State and federal jurisdiction
(b) Scope and application
   (1) Manufacturers, importers, distributors, manufacturing employers
   (2) General applicability to chemicals
   (3) Applicability to laboratories
   (4) Exemptions from labeling requirements
   (5) Excluded materials
(c) Definitions: Article, Assistant Secretary, Chemical, Chemical manufacturer, Chemical name, Combustible liquid, Common name, Compressed gas, Container, Designated representative, Director, Distributor, Employee, Employer, Explosive, Exposure, Flammable, Flashpoint, Foreseeable emergency, Hazard warning, Hazardous chemical, Health hazard, Identity, Immediate use, Importer, Label,

105

Manufacturing purchaser, Material safety data sheet, Mixture, Organic peroxide, Oxidizer, Physical hazard, Produce, Pyrophoric, Responsible party, Specific chemical identity, Trade secret, Unstable (reactive), Use, Water-reactive, Work area, Workplace

(d) Hazard determination
  (1) Responsibility
  (2) Basis
  (3) Regulation by reference
  (4) Determination of carcinogenicity
  (5) Evaluation of mixtures
  (6) Written description of methods
(e) Written hazard communication program
  (1) Employer responsibility
  (2) Use of existing written program
  (3) Required availability
(f) Labels and other forms of warning
  (1) Label content
  (2) Responsibility of chemical manufacturers, importers and distributors
  (3) Substance-specific requirements
  (4) Responsibility of manufacturing employers
  (5) Alternatives for stationary process containers
  (6) Exceptions for transfer containers
  (7) Defacing prohibited
  (8) Legibility and language
  (9) Status of existing labels
(g) Material safety data sheets
  (1) Responsibilities of various companies
  (2) Content
  (3) Unavailable information
  (4) Common sheets for related complex mixtures
  (5) Maintaining currency
  (6) Required transmission to purchasers
  (7) Obligations of distributors
  (8) Accessibility in the workplace
  (9) Form optional
  (10) Availability to OSHA
(h) Employee information and training
  (1) Information requirements
  (2) Training requirements

(i) Trade secrets
   (1) Conditions for withholding specific identity
   (2) Disclosure in emergencies
   (3) Disclosure for nonemergency needs
   (4) Content of confidentiality agreement
   (5) Noncontractual remedies
   (6) Disclosure to OSHA by health professional
   (7) Denial of request for disclosure
   (8) Appeal of denial to OSHA
   (9) Conditions to be considered by OSHA
   (10) Provisions for OSHA orders
   (11) Appeal to OSHA Review Commission
   (12) Disclosure to Assistant Secretary of Labor
   (13) Exemption of information about process or percentage mixture
(j) Effective dates
   (1) Chemical manufacturers and importers
   (2) Distributors
   (3) All manufacturing employers
Appendix A: Health Hazard Definitions (Mandatory)
   1. Carcinogen
   2. Corrosive
   3. Highly toxic
   4. Irritant
   5. Sensitizer
   6. Toxic
   7. Target organ effects
Appendix B: Hazard Determination (Mandatory)
   1. Carcinogenicity
   2. Human data
   3. Animal data
   4. Adequacy and reporting of data
Appendix C: Information Sources (Advisory)

TEXT OF THE STANDARD

§ 1910.1200   Hazard communication.

(a) *Purpose.* (1) The purpose of this section is to ensure that the hazards of all chemicals produced or imported by chemical manufacturers or importers are evaluated, and that information concerning their hazards is transmitted to affected employers and employees within the manufacturing sector. This transmittal of information is to be accomplished by means of comprehensive hazard communication programs, which are to include container labeling and other forms of warning, material safety data sheets and employee training.

(2) This occupational safety and health standard is intended to address comprehensively the issue of evaluating and communicating chemical hazards to employees in the manufacturing sector, and to preempt any state law pertaining to this subject. Any state which desires to assume responsibility in this area may only do so under the provisions of § 18 of the Occupational Safety and Health Act (29 U.S.C. 651 et. seq.) which deals with state jurisdiction and state plans.

(b) *Scope and application.* (1) This section requires chemical manufacturers or importers to assess the hazards of chemicals which they produce or import, and all employers in SIC Codes 20 through 39 (Division D, Standard Industrial Classification Manual) to provide information to their employees about the hazardous chemicals to which they are exposed, by means of a hazard communication program, labels and other forms of warning, material safety data sheets, and information and training. In addition, this section requires distributors to transmit the required information to employers in SIC Codes 20–39.

(2) This section applies to any chemical which is known to be present in the workplace in such a manner that employees may be exposed under normal conditions of use or in a foreseeable emergency.

(3) This section applies to laboratories only as follows:

(i) Employers shall ensure that labels on incoming containers of hazardous chemicals are not removed or defaced;

(ii) Employers shall maintain any material safety data sheets that are received with incoming shipments of hazardous chemicals, and ensure that they are readily accessible to laboratory employees; and,

(iii) Employers shall ensure that laboratory employees are apprised of the hazards of the chemicals in their workplaces in accordance with paragraph (h) of this section.

(4) This section does not require labeling of the following chemicals:

(i) Any pesticide as such term is defined in the Federal Insecticide, Fungicide, and Rodenticide Act (7 U.S.C. 136 et seq.), when subject to the labeling requirements of that Act and labeling regulations issued under that Act by the Environmental Protection Agency;

(ii) Any food, food additive, color additive, drug, or cosmetic, including materials intended for use as ingredients in such products (e.g., flavors and fragrances), as such terms are defined in the Federal Food, Drug, and Cosmetic Act (21 U.S.C. 301 et seq.) and regulations issued under that Act, when they are subject to the labeling requirements of that Act and labeling regulations issued under that Act by the Food and Drug Administration;

(iii) Any distilled spirits (beverage alcohols), wine, or malt beverage intended for nonindustrial use, as such terms are defined in the Federal Alcohol

Administration Act (27 U.S.C. 201 et seq.) and regulations issued under that Act, when subject to the labeling requirements of that Act and labeling regulations issued under that Act by the Bureau of Alcohol, Tobacco, and Firearms; and,

(iv) Any consumer product or hazardous substance as those terms are defined in the Consumer Product Safety Act (15 U.S.C. 2051 et seq.) and Federal Hazardous Substances Act (15 U.S.C. 1261 et seq.) respectively, when subject to a consumer product safety standard or labeling requirement of those Acts, or regulations issued under those Acts by the Consumer Product Safety Commission.

(5) This section does not apply to:

(i) Any hazardous waste as such term is defined by the Solid Waste Disposal Act, as amended by the Resource Conservation and Recovery Act of 1976, as amended (42 U.S.C. 6901 et seq.), when subject to regulations issued under that Act by the Environmental Protection Agency;

(ii) Tobacco or tobacco products;

(iii) Wood or wood products;

(iv) Articles; and,

(v) Foods, drugs, or cosmetics intended for personal consumption by employees while in the workplace.

(c) *Definitions.* "Article" means a manufactured item: (i) Which is formed to a specific shape or design during manufacture; (ii) which has end use function(s) dependent in whole or in part upon its shape or design during end use; and (iii) which does not release, or otherwise result in exposure to, a hazardous chemical under normal conditions of use.

"Assistant Secretary" means the Assistant Secretary of Labor for Occupational Safety and Health, U.S. Department of Labor, or designee.

"Chemical" means any element, chemical compound or mixture of elements and/or compounds.

"Chemical manufacturer" means an employer in SIC Codes 20 through 39 with a workplace where chemical(s) are produced for use or distribution.

"Chemical name" means the scientific designation of a chemical in accordance with the nomenclature system developed by the International Union of Pure and Applied Chemistry (IUPAC) or the Chemical Abstracts Service (CAS) rules of nomenclature, or a name which will clearly identify the chemical for the purpose of conducting a hazard evaluation.

"Combustible liquid" means any liquid having a flashpoint at or above 100°F (37.8°C), but below 200°F (93.3°C), except any mixture having components with flashpoints of 200°F (93.3°C), or higher, the total volume of which make up 99 percent or more of the total volume of the mixture.

"Common name" means any designation or identification such as code name, code number, trade name, brand name or generic name used to identify a chemical other than by its chemical name.

"Compressed gas" means:

(i) A gas or mixture of gases having, in a container, an absolute pressure exceeding 40 psi at 70°F (21.1°C); or

(ii) A gas or mixture of gases having, in a container, an absolute pressure exceeding 104 psi at 130°F (54.4°C) regardless of the pressure at 70°F (21.1°C); or

(iii) A liquid having a vapor pressure exceeding 40 psi at 100°F (37.8°C) as determined by ASTM D-323-72.

"Container" means any bag, barrel, bottle, box, can, cylinder, drum, reaction vessel, storage tank, or the like that containes a hazardous chemical. For purposes of this section, pipes or piping systems are not considered to be containers.

"Designated representative" means any individual or organization to whom an employee gives written authorization to exercise such employee's rights under this section. A recognized or certified collective bargaining agent shall be treated automatically as a designated representative without regard to written employee authorization.

"Director" means the Director, National Institute for Occupational Safety and Health, U.S. Department of Health and Human Services, or designee.

"Distributor" means a business, other than a chemical manufacturer or importer, which supplies hazardous chemicals to other distributors or to manufacturing purchasers.

"Employee" means a worker employed by an employer in a workplace in SIC Codes 20 through 39 who may be exposed to hazardous chemicals under normal operating conditions or foreseeable emergencies, including, but not limited to production workers, line supervisors, and repair or maintenance personnel. Office workers, grounds maintenance personnel, security personnel or non-resident management are generally not included, unless their job performance routinely involves potential exposure to hazardous chemicals.

"Employer" means a person engaged in a business within SIC Codes 20 through 39 where chemicals are either used, or are produced for use or distribution.

"Explosive" means a chemical that causes a sudden, almost instantaneous release of pressure, gas, and heat when subjected to sudden shock, pressure, or high temperature.

"Exposure" or "exposed" means that an employee is subjected to a hazardous chemical in the course of employment through any route of entry (inhalation, ingestion, skin contact or absorption, etc.), and includes potential (e.g., accidental or possible) exposure.

"Flammable" means a chemical that falls into one of the following categories:

(i) "Aerosol, flammable" means an aerosol that, when tested by the method described in 16 CFR 1500.45, yields a flame projection exceeding 18 inches at full valve opening, or a flashback (a flame extending back to the valve) at any degree of valve opening;

(ii) "Gas, flammable" means:

(A) A gas that, at ambient temperature and pressure, forms a flammable mixture with air at a concentration of thirteen (13) percent by volume or less; or

(B) A gas that, at ambient temperature and pressure, forms a range of flammable mixtures with air wider than twelve (12) percent by volume, regardless of the lower limit;

(iii) "Liquid, flammable" means any liquid having a flashpoint below 100°F (37.8°C), except any mixture having components with flashpoints of 100°F (37.8°C) or higher, the total of which make up 99 percent or more of the total volume of the mixture.

(iv) "Solid, flammable" means a solid, other than a blasting agent or explosive as defined in § 1910.109(a), that is liable to cause fire through friction, absorption of moisture, spontaneous chemical change, or retained heat from manufacturing or processing, or which can be ignited readily and when ignited burns so vigorously and persistently as to create a serious hazard. A chemical shall be considered to be a flammable solid if, when tested by the method described in 16 CFR 1500.44, it ignites and burns with a self-sustained flame at a rate greater than one-tenth of an inch per second along its major axis.

"Flashpoint" means the minimum temperature at which a liquid gives off a vapor in sufficient concentration to ignite when tested as follows:

(i) Tagliabue Closed Tester (See American National Standard Method of Test for Flash Point by Tag Closed Tester, Z11.24–1979 (ASTM D 56–79)) for liquids with a viscosity of less than 45 Saybolt Universal Seconds (SUS) at 100°F (37.8°C), that do not contain suspended solids and do not have a tendency to form a surface film under test; or

(ii) Pensky-Martens Closed Tester (see American National Standard Method of Test for Flash Point by Pensky-Martens Closed Tester, Z11.7–1979 (ASTM D 93–79)) for liquids with a viscosity equal to or greater than 45 SUS a 100°F (37.8°C), or that contain suspended solids, or that have a tendency to form a surface film under test; or

(iii) Setaflash Closed Tester (see American National Standard Method of Test for Flash Point by Setaflash Closed Tester (ASTM D 3278–78)).

Organic peroxides, which undergo autoaccelerating thermal decomposition, are excluded from any of the flashpoint determination methods specified above.

"Foreseeable emergency" means any potential occurrence such as, but not limited to, equipment failure, rupture of containers, or failure of control equipment which could result in an uncontrolled release of a hazardous chemical into the workplace.

"Hazard warning" means any words, pictures, symbols, or combination thereof appearing on a label or other appropriate form of warning which convey the hazards of the chemical(s) in the container(s).

"Hazardous chemical" means any chemical which is a physical hazard or a health hazard.

"Health hazard" means a chemical for which there is statistically significant evidence based on at least one study conducted in accordance with established scientific principles that acute or chronic health effects may occur in exposed employees. The term "health hazard" includes chemicals which are carcinogens, toxic or highly toxic agents, reproductive toxins, irritants, corrosives, sensitizers, hepatotoxins, nephrotoxins, neurotoxins, agents which act on the hematopoietic system, and agents which damage the lungs, skin, eyes, or mucous membranes. Appendix A provides further definitions and explanations of

the scope of health hazards covered by this section, and Appendix B describes the criteria to be used to determine whether or not a chemical is to be considered hazardous for purposes of this standard.

"Identity" means any chemical or common name which is indicated on the material safety data sheet (MSDS) for the chemical. The identity used shall permit cross-references to be made among the required list of hazardous chemicals, the label and the MSDS.

"Immediate use" means that the hazardous chemical will be under the control of and used only by the person who transfers it from a labeled container and only within the work shift in which it is transferred.

"Importer" means the first business with employees within the Customs Territory of the United States which receives hazardous chemicals produced in other countries for the purpose of supplying them to distributors or manufacturing purchasers within the United States.

"Label" means any written, printed, or graphic material displayed on or affixed to containers of hazardous chemicals.

"Manufacturing purchaser" means an employer with a workplace classified in SIC Codes 20 through 39 who purchases a hazardous chemical for use within that workplace.

"Material safety data sheet (MSDS)" means written or printed material concerning a hazardous chemical which is prepared in accordance with paragraph (g) of this section.

"Mixture" means any combination of two or more chemicals if the combination is not, in whole or in part, the result of a chemical reaction.

"Organic peroxide" means an organic compound that contains the bivalent -O-O-structure and which may be considered to be a structural derivative of hydrogen peroxide where one or both of the hydrogen atoms has been replaced by an organic radical.

"Oxidizer" means a chemical other than a blasting agent or explosive as defined in § 1910.109(a), that initiates or promotes combustion in other materials, thereby causing fire either of itself or through the release of oxygen or other gases.

"Physical hazard" means a chemical for which there is scientifically valid evidence that it is a combustible liquid, a compressed gas, explosive, flammable, an organic peroxide, an oxidizer, pyrophoric, unstable (reactive) or water-reactive.

"Produce" means to manufacture, process, formulate, or repackage.

"Pyrophoric" means a chemical that will ignite spontaneously in air at a temperature of 130° F (54.4° C) or below.

"Responsible party" means someone who can provide additional information on the hazardous chemical and appropriate emergency procedures, if necessary.

"Specific chemical identity" means the chemical name, Chemical Abstracts Service (CAS) Registry Number, or any other information that reveals the precise chemical designation of the substance.

"Trade secret" means any confidential formula, pattern, process, device, information or compilation of information (including chemical name or other unique chemical identifier) that is used in an employer's business, and that gives the employer an opportunity to obtain an advantage over competitors who do not know or use it.

"Unstable (reactive)" means a chemical which in the pure state, or as produced or transported, will vigorously polymerize, decompose, condense, or will become self-reactive under conditions of shocks pressure or temperature.

"Use" means to package, handle, react, or transfer.

"Water-reactive" means a chemical that reacts with water to release a gas that is either flammable or presents a health hazard.

"Work area" means a room or defined space in a workplace where hazardous chemicals are produced or used, and where employees are present.

"Workplace" means an establishment at one geographical location containing one or more work areas.

(d) *Hazard determination.* (1) Chemical manufacturers and importers shall evaluate chemicals produced in their workplaces or imported by them to determine if they are hazardous. Employers are not required to evaluate chemicals unless they choose not to rely on the evaluation performed by the chemical manufacturer or importer for the chemical to satisfy this requirement.

(2) Chemical manufacturers, importers or employers evaluating chemicals shall identify and consider the available scientific evidence concerning such hazards. For health hazards, evidence which is statistically significant and which is based on at least one positive study conducted in accordance with established scientific principles is considered to be sufficient to establish a hazardous effect if the results of the study meet the definitions of health hazards in this section. Appendix A shall be consulted for the scope of health hazards covered, and Appendix B shall be consulted for the criteria to be followed with respect to the completeness of the evaluation, and the data to be reported.

(3) The chemical manufacturer, importer or employer evaluating chemicals shall treat the following sources as establishing that the chemicals listed in them are hazardous:

(i) 29 CFR Part 1910, Subpart Z, Toxic and Hazardous Substances, Occupational Safety and Health Administration (OSHA); or,

(ii) *Threshold Limit Values for Chemical Substances and Physical*

Agents in the Work Environment,
American Conference of Governmental
Industrial Hygienists (ACGIH) (latest
edition).

The chemical manufacturer, importer, or
employer is still responsible for
evaluating the hazards associated with
the chemicals in these source lists in
accordance with the requirements of the
standard.

(4) Chemical manufacturers, importers
and employers evaluating chemicals
shall treat the following sources as
establishing that a chemical is a
carcinogen or potential carcinogen for
hazard communication purposes:

(i) National Toxicology Program
(NTP), *Annual Report on Carcinogens*
(latest edition);

(ii) International Agency for Research
on Cancer (IARC) *Monographs* (latest
editions); or

(iii) 29 CFR Part 1910, Subpart Z,
Toxic and Hazardous Substances,
Occupational Safety and Health
Administration.

Note.—The *Registry of Toxic Effects of
Chemical Substances* published by the
National Institute for Occupational Safety
and Health indicates whether a chemical has
been found by NTP or IARC to be a potential
carcinogen.

(5) The chemical manufacturer,
importer or employer shall determine
the hazards of mixtures of chemicals as
follows:

(i) If a mixture has been tested as a
whole to determine its hazards, the
results of such testing shall be used to
determine whether the mixture is
hazardous;

(ii) If a mixture has not been tested as
a whole to determine whether the
mixture is a health hazard, the mixture
shall be assumed to present the same
health hazards as do the components
which comprise one percent (by weight
or volume) or greater of the mixture,
except that the mixture shall be

assumed to present a carcinogenic
hazard if it contains a component in
concentrations of 0.1 percent or greater
which is considered to be a carcinogen
under paragraph (d)(4) of this section;

(iii) If a mixture has not been tested as
a whole to determine whether the
mixture is a physical hazard, the
chemical manufacturer, importer, or
employer may use whatever
scientifically valid data is available to
evaluate the physical hazard potential
of the mixture; and

(iv) If the employer has evidence to
indicate that a component present in the
mixture in concentrations of less than
one percent (or in the case of
carcinogens, less than 0.1 percent) could
be released in concentrations which
would exceed an established OSHA
permissible exposure limit or ACGIH
Threshold Limit Value, or could present
a health hazard to employees in those
concentrations, the mixture shall be
assumed to present the same hazard.

(6) Chemical manufacturers,
importers, or employers evaluating
chemicals shall describe in writing the
procedures they use to determine the
hazards of the chemical they evaluate.
The written procedures are to be made
available, upon request, to employees,
their designated representatives, the
Assistant Secretary and the Director.
The written description may be
incorporated into the written hazard
communication program required under
paragraph (e) of this section.

(e) *Written hazard communication
program.* (1) Employers shall develop
and implement a written hazard
communication program for their
workplaces which at least describes
how the criteria specified in paragraphs
(f), (g), and (h) of this section for labels
and other forms of warning, material
safety data sheets, and employee
information and training will be met,
and which also includes the following:

(i) A list of the hazardous chemicals

known to be present using an identity that is referenced on the appropriate material safety data sheet (the list may be compiled for the workplace as a whole or for individual work areas);

(ii) The methods the employer will use to inform employees of the hazards of non-routine tasks (for example, the cleaning of reactor vessels), and the hazards associated with chemicals contained in unlabeled pipes in their work areas; and,

(iii) The methods the employer will use to inform any contractor employers with employees working in the employer's workplace of the hazardous chemicals their employees may be exposed to while performing their work, and any suggestions for appropriate protective measures.

(2) The employer may rely on an existing hazard communication program to comply with these requirements, provided that it meets the criteria established in this paragraph (e).

(3) The employer shall make the written hazard communication program available, upon request, to employees, their designated representatives, the Assistant Secretary and the Director, in accordance with the requirements of 29 CFR 1910.20(e).

(f) *Labels and other forms of warning.* (1) The chemical manufacturer, importer, or distributor shall ensure that each container of hazardous chemicals leaving the workplace is labeled, tagged or marked with the following information:

(i) Identity of the hazardous chemical(s);

(ii) Appropriate hazard warnings; and

(iii) Name and address of the chemical manufacturer, importer, or other responsible party.

(2) Chemical manufacturers, importers, or distributors shall ensure that each container of hazardous chemicals leaving the workplace is labeled, tagged, or marked in accordance with this section in a manner which does not conflict with the requirements of the Hazardous Materials Transportation Act (18 U.S.C. 1801 et seq.) and regulations issued under that Act by the Department of Transportation.

(3) If the hazardous chemical is regulated by OSHA in a substance-specific health standard, the chemical manufacturer, importer, distributor or employer shall ensure that the labels or other forms of warning used are in accordance with the requirements of that standard.

(4) Except as provided in paragraphs (f)(5) and (f)(6) the employer shall ensure that each container of hazardous chemicals in the workplace is labeled, tagged, or marked with the following information:

(i) Identity of the hazardous chemical(s) contained therein; and

(ii) Appropriate hazard warnings.

(5) The employer may use signs, placards, process sheets, batch tickets, operating procedures, or other such written materials in lieu of affixing labels to individual stationary process containers, as long as the alternative method identifies the containers to which it is applicable and conveys the information required by paragraph (f)(4) of this section to be on a label. The written materials shall be readily accessible to the employees in their work area throughout each work shift.

(6) The employer is not required to label portable containers into which hazardous chemicals are transferred from labeled containers, and which are intended only for the immediate use of the employee who performs the transfer.

(7) The employer shall not remove or deface existing labels on incoming containers of hazardous chemicals, unless the container is immediately marked with the required information.

(8) The employer shall ensure that labels or other forms of warning are legible, in English, and prominently displayed on the container, or readily

available in the work area throughout each work shift. Employers having employees who speak other languages may add the information in their language to the material presented, as long as the information is presented in English as well.

(9) The chemical manufacturer, importer, distributor or employer need not affix new labels to comply with this section if existing labels already convey the required information.

(g) *Material safety data sheets.* (1) Chemical manufacturers and importers shall obtain or develop a material safety data sheet for each hazardous chemical they produce or import. Employers shall have a material safety data sheet for each hazardous chemical which they use.

(2) Each material safety data sheet shall be in English and shall contain at least the following information:

(i) The identity used on the label, and, except as provided for in paragraph (f) of this section on trade secrets:

(A) If the hazardous chemical is a single substance, its chemical and common name(s);

(B) If the hazardous chemical is a mixture which has been tested as a whole to determine its hazards, the chemical and common name(s) of the ingredients which contribute to these known hazards, and the common name(s) of the mixture itself; or,

(C) If the hazardous chemical is a mixture which has not been tested as a whole:

(*l*) The chemical and common name(s) of all ingredients which have been determined to be health hazards, and which comprise 1% or greater of the composition, except that chemicals identified as carcinogens under paragraph (d)(4) of this section shall be listed if the concentrations are 0.1% or greater; and,

(*2*) The chemical and common name(s) of all ingredients which have been

determined to present a physical hazard when present in the mixture;

(ii) Physical and chemical characteristics of the hazardous chemical (such as vapor pressure, flash point);

(iii) The physical hazards of the hazardous chemical, including the potential for fire, explosion, and reactivity;

(iv) The health hazards of the hazardous chemical, including signs and symptoms of exposure, and any medical conditions which are generally recognized as being aggravated by exposure to the chemical;

(v) The primary route(s) of entry;

(vi) The OSHA permissible exposure limit, ACGIH Threshold Limit Value, and any other exposure limit used or recommended by the chemical manufacturer, importer, or employer preparing the material safety data sheet, where available;

(vii) Whether the hazardous chemical is listed in the National Toxicology Program (NTP) *Annual Report on Carcinogens* (latest edition) or has been found to be a potential carcinogen in the International Agency for Research on Cancer (IARC) *Monographs* (latest editions), or by OSHA;

(viii) Any generally applicable precautions for safe handling and use which are known to the chemical manufacturer, importer or employer preparing the material safety data sheet, including appropriate hygienic practices, protective measures during repair and maintenance of contaminated equipment, and procedures for clean-up of spills and leaks;

(ix) Any generally applicable control measures which are known to the chemical manufacturer, importer or employer preparing the material safety data sheet, such as appropriate engineering controls, work practices, or personal protective equipment;

(x) Emergency and first aid procedures;

(xi) The date of preparation of the material safety data sheet or the last change to it; and,

(xii) The name, address and telephone number of the chemical manufacturer, importer, employer or other responsible party preparing or distributing the material safety data sheet, who can provide additional information on the hazardous chemical and appropriate emergency procedures, if necessary.

(3) If no relevant information is found for any given category on the material safety data sheet, the chemical manufacturer, importer or employer preparing the material safety data sheet shall mark it to indicate that no applicable information was found.

(4) Where complex mixtures have similar hazards and contents (i.e. the chemical ingredients are essentially the same, but the specific composition varies from mixture to mixture), the chemical manufacturer, importer or employer may prepare one material safety data sheet to apply to all of these similar mixtures.

(5) The chemical manufacturer, importer or employer preparing the material safety data sheet shall ensure that the information recorded accurately reflects the scientific evidence used in making the hazard determination. If the chemical manufacturer, importer or employer becomes newly aware of any significant information regarding the hazards of a chemical, or ways to protect against the hazards, this new information shall be added to the material safety data sheet within three months. If the chemical is not currently being produced or imported the chemical manufacturer or importer shall add the information to the material safety data sheet before the chemical is introduced into the workplace again.

(6) Chemical manufacturers or importers shall ensure that distributors and manufacturing purchasers of hazardous chemicals are provided an appropriate material safety data sheet with their initial shipment, and with the first shipment after a material safety data sheet is updated. The chemical manufacturer or importer shall either provide material safety data sheets with the shipped containers or send them to the manufacturing purchaser prior to or at the time of the shipment. If the material safety data sheet is not provided with the shipment, the manufacturing purchaser shall obtain one from the chemical manufacturer, importer, or distributor as soon as possible.

(7) Distributors shall ensure that material safety data sheets, and updated information, are provided to other distributors and manufacturing purchasers of hazardous chemicals.

(8) The employer shall maintain copies of the required material safety data sheets for each hazardous chemical in the workplace, and shall ensure that they are readily accessible during each work shift to employees when they are in their work area(s).

(9) Material safety data sheets may be kept in any form, including operating procedures, and may be designed to cover groups of hazardous chemicals in a work area where it may be more appropriate to address the hazards of a process rather than individual hazardous chemicals. However, the employer shall ensure that in all cases the required information is provided for each hazardous chemical, and is readily accessible during each work shift to employees when they are in their work area(s).

(10) Material safety data sheets shall also be made readily available, upon request, to designated representatives and to the Assistant Secretary, in accordance with the requirements of 29 CFR 1910.20(e). The Director shall also be given access to material safety data sheets in the same manner.

(h) *Employee information and*

training. Employers shall provide employees with information and training on hazardous chemicals in their work area at the time of their initial assignment, and whenever a new hazard is introduced into their work area.

(1) *Information.* Employees shall be informed of:

(i) The requirements of this section;

(ii) Any operations in their work area where hazardous chemicals are present; and,

(iii) The location and availability of the written hazard communication program, including the required list(s) of hazardous chemicals, and material safety data sheets required by this section.

(2) *Training.* Employee training shall include at least:

(i) Methods and observations that may be used to detect the presence or release of a hazardous chemical in the work area (such as monitoring conducted by the employer, continuous monitoring devices, visual appearance or odor of hazardous chemicals when being released, etc.);

(ii) The physical and health hazards of the chemicals in the work area;

(iii) The measures employees can take to protect themselves from these hazards, including specific procedures the employer has implemented to protect employees from exposure to hazardous chemicals, such as appropriate work practices, emergency procedures, and personal protective equipment to the used; and,

(iv) The details of the hazard communication program developed by the employer, including an explanation of the labeling system and the material safety data sheet, and how employees can obtain and use the appropriate hazard information.

(i) *Trade secrets.* (1) The chemical manufacturer, importer or employer may withhold the specific chemical identity, including the chemical name and other specific identification of a hazardous chemical, from the material safety data sheet, provided that:

(i) The claim that the information withheld is a trade secret can be supported;

(ii) Information contained in the material safety data sheet concerning the properties and effects of the hazardous chemical is disclosed;

. (iii) The material safety data sheet indicates that the specific chemical identity is being withheld as a trade secret; and,

(iv) The specific chemical identity is made available to health professionals, in accordance with the applicable provisions of this paragraph.

(2) Where a treating physician or nurse determines that a medical emergency exists and the specific chemical identity of a hazardous chemical is necessary for emergency or first-aid treatment, the chemical manufacturer, importer, or employer shall immediately disclose the specific chemical identity of a trade secret chemical to that treating physician or nurse, regardless of the existence of a written statement of need or a confidentiality agreement. The chemical manufacturer, importer, or employer may require a written statement of need and confidentiality agreement, in accordance with the provisions of paragraphs (i) (3) and (4) of this section, as soon as circumstances permit.

(3) In non-emergency situations, a chemical manufacturer, importer, or employer shall, upon request, disclose a specific chemical identity, otherwise permitted to be withheld under paragraph (i)(1) of this section, to a health professional (i.e. physician, industrial hygienist, toxicologist, or epidemiologist) providing medical or other occupational health services to exposed employee(s) if:

(i) the request is in writing;

(ii) The request describes with

reasonable detail one or more of the following occupational health needs for the information:

(A) To assess the hazards of the chemicals to which employees will be exposed;

(B) To conduct or assess sampling of the workplace atmosphere to determine employee exposure levels;

(C) To conduct pre-assignment or periodic medical surveillance of exposed employees;

(D) To provide medical treatment to exposed employees;

(E) To select or assess appropriate personal protective equipment for exposed employees;

(F) To design or assess engineering controls or other protective measures for exposed employees; and,

(G) To conduct studies to determine the health effects of exposure.

(iii) The request explains in detail why the disclosure of the specific chemical identity is essential and that, in lieu thereof, the disclosure of the following information would not enable the health professional to provide the occupational health services described in paragraph (ii) of this section:

(A) The properties and effects of the chemical;

(B) Measures for controlling workers' exposure to the chemical;

(C) Methods of monitoring and analyzing worker exposure to the chemical; and,

(D) Methods of diagnosing and treating harmful exposures to the chemical;

(iv) The request includes a description of the procedures to be used to maintain the confidentiality of the disclosed information; and,

(v) The health professional, and the employer or contractor of the health professional's services (i.e., downstream employer, labor organization, or individual employer), agree in a written confidentiality agreement that the health professional will not use the trade secret information for any purpose other than the health need(s) asserted and agree not to release the information under any circumstances other than to OSHA, as provided in paragraph (i)(6) of this section, except as authorized by the terms of the agreement or by the chemical manufacturer, importer, or employer.

(4) The confidentiality agreement authorized by paragraph (i)(3)(iv) of this section:

(i) May restrict the use of the information to the health purposes indicated in the written statement of need;

(ii) May provide for appropriate legal remedies in the event of a breach of the agreement, including stipulation of a reasonable pre-estimate of likely damages; and,

(iii) May not include requirements for the posting of a penalty bond.

(5) Nothing in this standard is meant to preclude the parties from pursuing non-contractual remedies to the extent permitted by law.

(6) If the health professional receiving the trade secret information decides that there is a need to disclose it to OSHA, the chemical manufacturer, importer, or employer who provided the information shall be informed by the health professional prior to, or at the same time as, such disclosure.

(7) If the chemical manufacturer, importer, or employer denies a written request for disclosure of a specific chemical identity, the denial must:

(i) Be provided to the health professional within thirty days of the request;

(ii) Be in writing;

(iii) Include evidence to support the claim that the specific chemical identity is a trade secret;

(iv) State the specific reasons why the request is being denied; and,

(v) Explain in detail how alternative information may satisfy the specific medical or occupational healtn need without revealing the specific chemical identity.

(8) The health professional whose request for information is denied under paragraph (i)(3) of this section may refer the request and the written denial of the request to OSHA for consideration.

(9) When a health professional refers the denial to OSHA under paragraph (i)(8) of this section, OSHA shall consider the evidence to determine if:

(i) The chemical manufacturer, importer, or employer has supported the claim that the specific chemical identity is a trade secret;

(ii) The health professional has supported the claim that there is a medical or occupational health need for the information; and,

(iii) The health professional has demonstrated adequate means to protect the confidentiality.

(10) (i) If OSHA determines that the specific chemical identity requested under paragraph (i)(3) of this section is not a bona fide trade secret, or that it is a trade secret but the requesting health professional has a legitimate medical or occupational health need for the information, has executed a written confidentiality agreement, and has shown adequate means to protect the confidentiality of the information, the chemical manufacturer, importer, or employer will be subject to citation by OSHA.

(ii) If a chemical manufacturer, importer, or employer demonstrates to OSHA that the execution of a confidentiality agreement would not provide sufficient protection against the potential harm from the unauthorized disclosure of a trade secret specific chemical identity, the Assistant Secretary may issue such orders or impose such additional limitations or conditions upon the disclosure of the requested chemical information as may be appropriate to assure that the

occupational health services are provided without an undue risk of harm to the chemical manufacturer, importer, or employer.

(11) If, following the issuance of a citation and any protective orders, the chemical manufacturer, importer, or employer continues to withhold the information, the matter is referrable to the Occupational Safety and Health Review Commission for enforcement of the citation. In accordance with Commission rules, the Administrative Law Judge may review the citation and supporting documentation in camera or issue appropriate protective orders.

(12) Notwithstanding the existence of a trade secret claim, a chemical manufacturer, importer, or employer shall, upon request, disclose to the Assistant Secretary any information which this section requires the chemical manufacturer, importer, or employer to make available. Where there is a trade secret claim, such claim shall be made no later than at the time the information is provided to the Assistant Secretary so that suitable determinations of trade secret status can be made and the necessary protections can be implemented.

(13) Nothing in this paragraph shall be construed as requiring the disclosure under any circumstances of process or percentage of mixture information which is trade secret.

(j) Effective dates. Employers shall be in compliance with this section within the following time periods:

(1) Chemical manufacturers and importers shall label containers of hazardous chemicals leaving their workplaces, and provide material safety data sheets with initial shipments by November 25, 1985.

(2) Distributors shall be in compliance with all provisions of this section applicable to them by November 25, 1985.

(3) Employers shall be in compliance

with all provisions of this section by May 25, 1986, including initial training for all current employees.

Appendix A to § 1910.1200—Health Hazard Definitions (Mandatory)

Although safety hazards related to the physical characteristics of a chemical can be objectively defined in terms of testing requirements (e.g. flammability), health hazard definitions are less precise and more subjective. Health hazards may cause measurable changes in the body—such as decreased pulmonary function. These changes are generally indicated by the occurrence of signs and symptoms in the exposed employees—such as shortness of breath, a non-measurable, subjective feeling. Employees exposed to such hazards must be apprised of both the change in body function and the signs and symptoms that may occur to signal that change.

The determination of occupational health hazards is complicated by the fact that many of the effects or signs and symptoms occur commonly in non-occupationally exposed populations, so that effects of exposure are difficult to separate from normally occurring illnesses. Occasionally, a substance causes an effect that is rarely seen in the population at large, such as angiosarcomas caused by vinyl chloride exposure, thus making it easier to ascertain that the occupational exposure was the primary causative factor. More often, however, the effects are common, such as lung cancer. The situation is further complicated by the fact that most chemicals have not been adequately tested to determine their health hazard potential, and data do not exist to substantiate these effects.

There have been many attempts to categorize effects and to define them in various ways. Generally, the terms "acute" and "chronic" are used to delineate between effects on the basis of severity or duration. "Acute" effects usually occur rapidly as a result of short-term exposures, and are of short duration. "Chronic" effects generally occur as a result of long-term exposure, and are of long duration.

The acute effects referred to most frequently are those defined by the American National Standards Institute (ANSI) standard for Precautionary Labeling of Hazardous Industrial Chemicals (Z129.1–1982)—irritation, corrosivity, sensitization and lethal dose. Although these are important health effects, they do not adequately cover the considerable range of acute effects which may occur as a result of occupational exposure, such as, for example, narcosis.

Similarly, the term chronic effect is often used to cover only carcinogenicity, teratogenicity, and mutagenicity. These effects are obvious a concern in the workplace, but again, do not adequately cover the area of chronic effects, excluding, for example, blood dyscrasias (such as anemia), chronic bronchitis and liver atrophy.

The goal of defining precisely, in measurable terms, every possible health effect that may occur in the workplace as a result of chemical exposures cannot realistically be accomplished. This does not negate the need for employees to be informed of such effects and protected from them.

Appendix B, which is also mandatory, outlines the principles and procedures of hazard assessment.

For purposes of this section, any chemicals which meet any of the following definitions, as determined by the criteria set forth in Appendix B are health hazards:

1. *Carcinogen:* A chemical is considered to be a carcinogen if:

(a) It has been evaluated by the International Agency for Research on Cancer (IARC), and found to be a carcinogen or potential carcinogen; or

(b) It is listed as a carcinogen or potential carcinogen in the *Annual*

Report on Carcinogens published by the National Toxicology Program (NTP) (latest edition); or,

(c) It is regulated by OSHA as a carcinogen.

2. *Corrosive:* A chemical that causes visible destruction of, or irreversible alterations in, living tissue by chemical action at the site of contact. For example, a chemical is considered to be corrosive if, when tested on the intact skin of albino rabbits by the method described by the U.S. Department of Transportation in Appendix A to 49 CFR Part 173, it destroys or changes irreversibly the structure of the tissue at the site of contact following an exposure period of four hours. This term shall not refer to action on inanimate surfaces.

3. *Highly toxic:* A chemical falling within any of the following categories:

(a) A chemical that has a median lethal dose (LD_{50}) of 50 milligrams or less per kilogram of body weight when administered orally to albino rats weighing between 200 and 300 grams each.

(b) A chemical that has a median lethal dose (LD_{50}) of 200 milligrams or less per kilogram of body weight when administered by continuous contact for 24 hours (or less if death occurs within 24 hours) with the bare skin of albino rabbits weighing between two and three kilograms each.

(c) A chemical that has a median lethal concentration (LC_{50}) in air of 200 parts per million by volume or less of gas or vapor, or 2 milligrams per liter or less of mist, fume, or dust, when administered by continuous inhalation for one hour (or less if death occurs within one hour) to albino rats weighing between 200 and 300 grams each.

4. *Irritant:* A chemical, which is not corrosive, but which causes a reversible inflammatory effect on living tissue by chemical action at the site of contact. A chemical is a skin irritant if, when tested on the intact skin of albino rabbits by the methods of 16 CFR 1500.41 for four hours exposure or by other appropriate techniques, it results in an empirical score of five or more. A chemical is an eye irritant if so determined under the procedure listed in 16 CFR 1500.42 or other appropriate techniques.

5. *Sensitizer:* A chemical that causes a substantial proportion of exposed people or animals to develop an allergic reaction in normal tissue after repeated exposure to the chemical.

6. *Toxic.* A chemical falling within any of the following categories:

(a) A chemical that has a median lethal dose (LD_{50}) of more than 50 milligrams per kilogram but not more than 500 milligrams per kilogram of body weight when administered orally to albino rats weighing between 200 and 300 grams each.

(b) A chemical that has a median lethal dose (LD_{50}) of more than 200 milligrams per kilogram but not more than 1,000 milligrams per kilogram of body weight when administered by continuous contact for 24 hours (or less if death occurs within 24 hours) with the bare skin of albino rabbits weighing between two and three kilograms each.

(c) A chemical that has a median lethal concentration (LC_{50}) in air of more than 200 parts per million but not more than 2,000 parts per million by volume of gas or vapor, or more than two milligrams per liter but not more than 20 milligrams per liter of mist, fume, or dust, when administered by continuous inhalation for one hour (or less if death occurs within one hour) to albino rats weighing between 200 and 300 grams each.

7. *Target organ effects.* The following is a target organ categorization of effects which may occur, including examples of signs and symptons and chemicals which have been found to cause such effects. These examples are presented to illustrate the range and diversity of effects and hazards found in the

workplace, and the broad scope employers must consider in this area, but are not intended to be all-inclusive.

a Hepatotoxins:	Chemicals which produce liver damage.
Signs and Symptons:	Jaundice; liver enlargement.
Chemicals:	Carbon tetrachloride; nitrosamines.
b Nephrotoxins:	Chemicals which produce kidney damage.
Signs and Symptons:	Edema, proteinuria.
Chemicals:	Halogenated hydrocarbons; uranium
c. Neurotoxins:	Chemicals which produce their primary toxic effects on the nervous system.
Signs and Symptons:	Narcosis; behavioral changes; decrease in motor functions.
Chemicals:	Mercury; carbon disulfide.
d. Agents which act on the blood or hematopoietic system:.	Decrease hemoglobin function; deprive the body tissues of oxygen.
Signs and Symptons.	Cyanosis; loss of consciousness.
Chemicals:	Carbon monoxide; cyanides.
e. Agents which damage the lung:	Chemicals which irritate or damage the pulmonary tissue.
Signs and Symptons:	Cough; tightness in chest, shortness of breath.
Chemicals.	Silica; asbestos.
f Reproductive toxins:	Chemicals which affect the reproductive capabilities including chromosomal damage (mutations) and effects on fetuses (teratogenesis).
Signs and Symptons:	Birth defects; sterility.
Chemicals:	Lead; DBCP.
g Cutaneous hazards.	Chemical which affect the dermal layer of the body.
Signs and Symptons:	Defatting of the skin, rashes; irritation.
Chemicals:	Ketones; chlorinated compounds.
h. Eye hazards:	Chemicals which affect the eye or visual capacity.
Signs and Symptons.	Conjunctivitis; corneal damage.
Chemicals:	Organic solvents; acids.

Appendix B to § 1900.1200—Hazard Determination (Mandatory)

The quality of a hazard communication program is largely dependent upon the adequacy and accuracy of the hazard determination. The hazard determination requirement of this standard is performance-oriented. Chemical manufacturers, importers, and employers evaluating chemicals are not required to follow any specific methods for determining hazards, but they must be able to demonstrate that they have adequately ascertained the hazards of the chemicals produced or imported in accordance with the criteria set forth in this Appendix.

Hazard evaluation is a process which relies heavily on the professional judgment of the evaluator, particularly in the area of chronic hazards. The performance-orientation of the hazard determination does diminish the duty of the chemical manufacturer, importer or employer to conduct a thorough evaluation, examining all relevant data and producing a scientifically defensible evaluation. For purposes of this standard, the following criteria shall be used in making hazard determinations that meet the requirements of this standard.

1. *Carcinogenicity:* As described in paragraph (d)(4) and Appendix A of this section, a determination by the National Toxicology Program, the International Agency for Research on Cancer, or OSHA that a chemical is a carcinogen or potential carcinogen will be considered conclusive evidence for purposes of this section.

2. *Human data:* Where available, epidemiological studies and case reports of adverse health effects shall be considered in the evaluation.

3. *Animal data:* Human evidence of

health effects in exposed populations is generally not available for the majority of chemicals produced or used in the workplace. Therefore, the available results of toxicological testing in animal populations shall be used to predict the health effects that may be experienced by exposed workers. In particular, the definitions of certain acute hazards refer to specific animal testing results (see Appendix A).

4. *Adequacy and reporting of data:* The results of any studies which are designed and conducted according to established scientific principles, and which report statistically significant conclusions regarding the health effects of a chemical, shall be a sufficient basis for a hazard determination and reported on any material safety data sheet. The chemical manufacturer, importer, or employer may also report the results of other scientifically valid studies which tend to refute the findings of hazard.

Appendix C to § 1900.1200—Information Sources (Advisory)

The following is a list of available data sources which the chemical manufacturer, importer, or employer may wish to consult to evaluate the hazards of chemicals they produce or import:

— Any information in their own company files such as toxicity testing results or illness experience of company employees.

— Any information obtained from the supplier of the chemical, such as material safety data sheets or product safety bulletins.

— Any pertinent information obtained from the following source list (latest editions should be used):

Condensed Chemical Dictionary
Van Nostrand Reinhold Co., 135 West 50th Street, New York, NY 10020
The Merck Index: An Encyclopedia of Chemicals and Drugs
Merck and Company, Inc., 126 E. Lincoln Avenue, Rahway, NJ 07065
IARC Monographs on the Evaluation of the Carcinogenic Risk of Chemicals to Man

Geneva: World Health Organization, International Agency for Research on Cancer, 1972–1977. (Multivolume work), 49 Sheridan Street, Albany, New York
Industrial Hygiene and Toxicology, by F. A. Patty
John Wiley & Sons, Inc., New York, NY (Five volumes)
Clinical Toxicology of Commercial Products
Gleason, Gosselin and Hodge
Casarett and Doull's Toxicology; The Basic Science of Poisons
Doull, Klaassen, and Amdur, Macmillan Publishing Co., Inc., New York, NY
Industrial Toxicology, by Alice Hamilton and Harriet L. Hardy
Publishing Sciences Group, Inc., Acton, MA
Toxicology of the Eye, by W. Morton Grant
Charles C. Thomas, 301–327 East Lawrence Avenue, Springfield, IL
Recognition of Health Hazards in Industry
William A. Burgess, John Wiley and Sons, 605 Third Avenue, New York, NY 10158
Chemical Hazards of the Workplace
Nick H. Proctor and James P. Hughes, J. P. Lipincott Company, 6 Winchester Terrace, New York, NY 10022
Handbook of Chemistry and Physics
Chemical Rubber Company, 18901 Cranwood Parkway, Cleveland, OH 44128
Threshold Limit Values for Chemical Substances and Physical Agents in the Workroom Environment with Intended Changes
American Conference of Governmental Industrial Hygienists, 6500 Glenway Avenue, Bldg. D–5, Cincinnati, OH 45211

Note.—The following documents are on sale by the Superintendent of Documents, U.S. Government Printing Office, Washington, D.C. 20402.

Occupational Health Guidelines
NIOSH/OSHA (NIOSH Pub. No. 81–123)
NIOSH/OSHA Pocket Guide to Chemical Hazards
NIOSH Pub. No. 78–210
Registry of Toxic Effects of Chemical Substances
U.S. Department of Health and Human Services, Public Health Service, Center for Disease Control, National Institute for Occupational Safety and Health (NIOSH Pub. No. 80–102)

The Industrial Environment—Its Evaluation and Control
U.S. Department of Health and Human Services, Public Health Service, Center for Disease Control, National Institute for Occupational Safety and Health (NIOSH Pub. No. 74–117)
Miscellaneous Documents—National Institute for Occupational Safety and Health
1. Criteria for a recommended standard * * * Occupational Exposure to "———"
2. Special Hazard Reviews
3. Occupational Hazard Assessment
4. Current Intelligence Bulletins

Bibliographic Data BAses

Service Provider and *File Name*

Bibliographic Retrieval Services (BRS), Corporation Park, Bldg. 702, Scotia, New York 12302
AGRICOLA
BIOSIS PREVIEWS
CA CONDENSATES
CA SEARCH
DRUG INFORMATION
MEDLARS
MEDOC
NTIS
POLLUTION ABSTRACTS
SCIENCE CITATION INDEX
SSIE
Lockheed—DIALOG, Lockheed Missiles & Space Company, Inc., P.O. Box 44481, San Francisco, CA 94144
AGRICOLA
BIOSIS PREV. 1972–PRESENT
BIOSIS PREV. 1969–71
CA CONDENSATES 1970–71
CA SEARCH 1972–76
CA SEARCH 1977–PRESENT
CHEMNAME
CONFERENCE PAPERS INDEX

FOOD SCIENCE & TECH. ABSTR.
FOODS ADLIBRA
INTL. PHARMACEUTICAL ABSTR.
NTIS
POLLUTION ABSTRACTS
SCISEARCH 1978–PRESENT
SCISEARCH 1974–77
SSIE CURRENT RESEARCH
SDC—ORBIT, SDC Search Service, Department No. 2230, Pasadena, CA 91051
AGRICOLA
BIOCODES
BIOSIS/BIO6973
CAS6771/CAS7276
CAS77
CHEMDEX
CONFERENCE
ENVIROLINE
LABORDOC
NTIS
POLLUTION
SSIE
Chemical Information System (CIS), Chemical Information Systems Inc., 7215 Yorke Road, Baltimore, MD 21212
Structure & Nomeclature Search System
Acute Toxicity (RTECS)
Clinical Toxicology of Commercial Products
Oil and Hazardous Materials Technical Assistance Data System
National Library of Medicine, Department of Health and Human Services, Public Health Service, National Institutes of Health, Bethesda, MD 20209
Toxicology Data Bank (TDB)
MEDLIN
TOXLINE
CANCERLIT
RTECS

APPENDIX 2
SUGGESTED MSDS FORM
FOR GENERAL USE

In developing the Hazard Communication Standard, OSHA did not prescribe a specific form to be used for Material Safety Data Sheets. For most of the regulated community, that omission is a great inconvenience. It is easier, and more comfortable, to use a standard, prescribed form than it is to develop your own, particularly if you do not have your own staff of chemists, industrial hygienists, or health professionals.

A natural reaction might be to use the MSDS form previously designed by OSHA for the shipbuilding industry, known as OSHA Form 20. But to do so would be a serious mistake, because a number of entries required by this Standard are absent from Form 20. A copy of this form is reprinted in Chapter 7 for you to see what it looks like, but it should NOT be used.

A new, suitable MSDS form has been designed and is presented here in full, double-page size for your convenience. This particular form has blanks for all the information required under this Standard. In addition, the various information sections of this form are arranged in such a way that the hazard information and control data are quickly and easily located and interpreted. The other supporting data and information are still present but are positioned in such a way as not to interfere with the process of looking up the data that are more commonly sought. Few, if any, other MSDS forms have this feature.

You are invited to copy this form and use it in your own company's Hazard Communication Program.

MATERIAL SAFETY DATA SHEET

Section 1.   Identity of Material

PRODUCT NAME OR NUMBER	
SYNONYMS	

FORMULA	CAS NUMBER	CHEMICAL FAMILY

REGULATED IDENTIFICATION	DOT PROPER SHIPPING NAME
	SHIPPING ID NUMBER UN NA EPA HAZARDOUS WASTE ID NUMBER

HAZARDOUS INGREDIENTS	%	CAS NUMBER

Section 2.   Hazard Specifications

KNOWN HAZARDS UNDER 29 CFR 1910.1200								
	YES	NO		YES	NO	TLV =	ppm,	mg/m³
COMBUSTIBLE LIQUID			SKIN HAZARD			PEL =	ppm,	mg/m³
FLAMMABLE MATERIAL			EYE HAZARD			NFPA HAZARD SIGNAL		
PYROPHORIC MATERIAL			TOXIC AGENT			HEALTH		FLAMMABILITY
EXPLOSIVE MATERIAL			HIGHLY TOXIC AGENT					
UNSTABLE MATERIAL			SENSITIZER			STABILITY		SPECIAL
WATER REACTIVE MATERIAL			CARCINOGEN			DOT HAZARD CLASS		
OXIDIZER			REPRODUCTIVE TOXIN					
ORGANIC PEROXIDE			BLOOD TOXIN					
CORROSIVE MATERIAL			NERVOUS SYSTEM TOXIN			EPA HAZARD WASTE CLASS		
COMPRESSED GAS			LUNG TOXIN					
IRRITANT			LIVER TOXIN					
			KIDNEY TOXIN					

Section 3.   Safe Usage Data

PROTECTIVE EQUIPMENT TYPES	EYES	
	RESPIRATORY	
	GLOVES	
	OTHER	
VENTILATION	GENERAL MECHANICAL	
	LOCAL EXHAUST	
PRECAUTIONS	HANDLING & STORAGE	
	OTHER	

LEWIS PUBLISHERS GRANTS PERMISSION TO USE THIS FORM, WHICH IS DESIGNED TO COMPLY WITH THE MSDS REQUIREMENTS OF 29 CFR 1910.1200.

Section 4.   Emergency Response Data

FIRE	EXTINGUISHING MEDIA	
	SPECIAL PROCEDURES	
	UNUSUAL HAZARDS	
EXPOSURE	FIRST AID MEASURES	
SPILLS	STEPS TO BE TAKEN	
RQ =	WASTE DISPOSAL METHOD	

Section 5.   Physical Hazard Data

FLAMMABILITY	LFL =	%	FLASH POINT	°F °C
	UFL =	%	METHOD USED	
STABILITY	STABLE		CONDITIONS TO AVOID	
	UNSTABLE		HAZARDOUS DECOMP. PDTS	
HAZARDOUS POLYMERIZATION	MAY OCCUR		CONDITIONS TO AVOID	
	WILL NOT OCCUR			
INCOMPATIBILITY	MATERIALS TO AVOID			

Section 6.   Health Hazard Data

EFFECTS OF EXPOSURE
EMERGENCY TREATMENT

Section 7.   Physical and Chemical Properties

BOILING PT =	°F	°C	VAPOR DENSITY (AIR 1)	VOLATILE COMPONENTS	
VAPOR PRESS =	mmHg	psi	pH		
SOLUBILITY IN H₂O			WILL DISSOLVE IN	EVAPORATION RATE (=1)	
APPEARANCE				IS MATERIAL PASTE	POWDER
ODOR				SOLID LIQUID	GAS

Section 8.   Manufacturer or Supplier Data

FIRM'S NAME & MAILING ADDRESS	NAME (PRINT)
	SIGNATURE
	TITLE
	DATE
	EMERGENCY TELEPHONE NO.

APPENDIX 3
SUBSTANCES REGULATED BY REFERENCE

The substances listed below are specifically included in the Federal OSHA Hazard Communication Standard (29 CFR 1910.1200) by reference. Either they are listed by ACGIH in the 1984-85 TLVs booklet, or they are previously regulated by OSHA in 29 CFR 1910.1000-1047. It should be noted that many of these substances are sold and used under two or more different, equally "correct" names. In general, only one common name for each substance has been used in this list. Thus, if a substance is not found under the first name searched, all possible synonyms should be searched before deciding that the substance is not included in the list.

NOTE: An estimated seventy to eighty thousand additional substances are regulated by performance definition under the Standard, even though they are not to be found in the following list. Therefore, it is necessary to use much CAUTION before deciding that a particular substance is not covered by the Standard. In addition, the TLV list is updated and modified annually, and the OSHA tables are also changed periodically. Therefore, it is essential that the latest editions of these lists be consulted before it is assumed that a particular substance is not regulated by reference.

Acetaldehyde
Acetic acid
Acetic anhydride
Acetone
Acetonitrile
2-Acetylaminofluorene
Acetylene

Acetylene tetrabromide
Acetylene tetrachloride
Acrolein
Acrylamide
Acrylic acid
Acrylonitrile
Aldrin

Allyl alcohol
Allyl chloride
Allyl glycidyl ether
Allyl propyl disulfide
alpha-Alumina
Aluminum alkyls (NOC)
Aluminum metal
Aluminum Pyro powders
Aluminum salts, soluble
4-Aminodiphenyl
2-Aminopyridine
Amitrole
Ammonia
Ammonium chloride
Ammonium sulfamate
Amosite asbestos
Amyl acetate
Aniline
Aniline homologs
o-Anisidine
p-Anisidine
Antimony
Antimony compounds
Argon
Arsenic
Arsenic compounds, organic
Arsenic compounds, soluble
Arsenic trioxide
Arsine
Asbestos, NOS
Asphalt fumes
Aspirin
Atrazine
Azinphos-methyl

Barium compounds, soluble
Barium sulfate
Benomyl
Benzene
1,3-Benzenedimethanamine
Benzidine

Benzo(a)pyrene
Benzoquinone
Benzoyl peroxide
Benzyl chloride
Beryllium
Beryllium compounds
Biphenyl-Phenyl ether mixture
Bismuth telluride
Borates, tetra, sodium salts
Boron oxide
Boron tribromide
Boron trifluoride
Bromacil
Bromine
Bromine pentafluoride
Bromochloromethane
Bromoform
Bromotrifluoromethane
Butadiene
Butane
2-Butoxyethanol
Butyl acetate
Butyl acrylate
Butyl alcohol
Butylamine
Butylated hydroxytoluene
tert-Butyl chromate
n-Butyl glycidyl ether
n-Butyl lactate
Butyl mercaptan
Butyl methyl ketone
o-sec-Butylphenol
p-tert-Butyltoluene

Cadmium
Cadmium oxide
Cadmium salts
Calcium cyanamide
Calcium hydroxide
Calcium silicate
Camphor

Caprolactam
Captafol
Captan
Carbaryl
Carbofuran
Carbon black
Carbon dioxide
Carbon disulfide
Carbon monoxide
Carbon tetrabromide
Carbon tetrachloride
Carbonyl fluoride
Catechol
Caustic potash
Caustic soda
Cesium hydroxide
Chlordane
Chlorinated diphenyl oxide
Chlorine
Chlorine dioxide
Chlorine trifluoride
Chloroacetaldehyde
Chloroacetophenone
Chloroacetyl chloride
Chlorobenzene
Chlorodifluoromethane
Chlorodiphenyls
bis(Chloroethyl) ether
Chloroform
bis(Chloromethyl) ether
Chloromethyl methyl ether
1-Chloro-1-nitropropane
Chloropentafluoroethane
Chloropicrin
Chloroprene
o-Chlorostyrene
o-Chlorotoluene
Chlorpyrifos
Chromates
Chromic acid
Chromite ore processing

Chromous compounds
Chromic compounds
Chromium(VI) compounds
Chromium metal
Chromium oxychloride
Chrysene
Chrysotile asbestos
Clopidol
Coal
Coal tar
Cobalt carbonyl
Cobalt hydrocarbonyl
Cobalt metal
Coke oven emissions
Copper metal
Cotton, raw
Cresol, all isomers
Cristobalite (silica)
Crocidolite asbestos
Crotonaldehyde
Crufomate
Cumene
Cyanamide
Cyanides
Cyanogen
Cyanogen chloride
Cyclohexane
Cyclohexanol
Cyclohexanone
Cyclohexene
Cyclohexylamine
Cyclonite
1,3-Cyclopentadiene
Cyclopentane
Cyhexatin
2,4-D
DDT
Decaborane
Demeton
Diacetone alcohol
Diatomaceous earth

Diazinon
Diazomethane
Diborane
1,2-Dibromo-3-chloropropane
Dibromodifluoromethane
2-(dibutylamino)ethanol
Dibutyl phosphate
Dibutyl phthalate
Dichloroacetylene
o-Dichlorobenzene
p-Dichlorobenzene
3,3'-Dichlorobenzidine
Dichlorodifluoromethane
1,3-Dichloro-5,5-dimethylhydantoin
1,1-Dichloroethane
1,2-Dichloroethylene
Dichlorofluoromethane
1,1-Dichloro-1-nitroethane
Dichloropropene
2,2-Dichloropropionic acid
1,2-Dichloro-1,1,2,2-
    tetrafluoroethane
Dichlorvos
Dicrotophos
Dicyclopentadiene
Dieldrin
Diethanolamine
Diethylamine
Diethylaminoethanol
Diethylene triamine
Diethyl ketone
Diethyl phthalate
Diglycidyl ether
Diisobutyl ketone
Diisopropylamine
Dimethyl acetamide
Dimethylamine
4-Dimethylaminoazobenzene
Dimethylaniline
Dimethyl carbamoyl chloride
Dimethylformamide

1,1-Dimethylhydrazine
Dimethylnitrosoamine
Dimethylphthalate
Dimethyl sulfate
Dinitolmide
Dinitrobenzene
4,6-Dinitro-o-cresol
2,4-Dinitrotoluene
Dioctyl phthalate
Dioxane
Dioxathion
Diphenyl
Diphenylamine
4,4'-Diphenylmethane diisocyanate
Dipropylene glycol monomethyl ether
Dipropyl ketone
Diquat
Disulfoton
Diuron
Divinyl benzene

Emery
Endosulfan
Endrin
Epichlorohydrin
EPN
Ethane
Ethanolamine
Ethion
Ethyl acetate
Ethyl acrylate
Ethyl alcohol
Ethylamine
Ethyl amyl ketone
Ethyl benzene
Ethyl bromide
Ethyl butyl ketone
Ethyl chloride
Ethylene
Ethylene chlorohydrin
Ethylenediamine

Ethylene dibromide
Ethylene dichloride
Ethylene glycol
Ethylene glycol dinitrate
Ethylene glycol monoethyl ether
Ethylene glycol monoethyl ether
  acetate
Ethylene glycol monoisopropyl ether
Ethylene glycol monomethyl ether
Ethyleneimine
Ethylene oxide
Ethyl ether
Ethyl formate
Ethylidene norbornene
Ethyl mercaptan
N-Ethylmorpholine
Ethyl silicate

Fensulfothion
Fenthion
Ferbam
Ferrocene
Ferrovanadium
Fibrous glass
Fluorides
Fluorine
Fonofos
Formaldehyde
Formamide
Formic acid
Furfural
Furfuryl alcohol
Gasoline
Germane
Glutaraldehyde
Glycerin
Glycidol
Graphite
Gypsum

Hafnium

Helium
Heptachlor
Heptane
Hexachlorobutadiene
Hexachlorocyclopentadiene
Hexachloroethane
Hexachloronaphthalene
Hexafluoroacetone
Hexamethyl phosphoramide
Hexane
sec-Hexyl acetate
Hexylene glycol
Hydrazine
Hydrocyanic acid
Hydrogen
Hydrogenated terphenyls
Hydrogen bromide
Hydrogen chloride
Hydrogen cyanide
Hydrogen fluoride
Hydrogen peroxide
Hydrogen selenide
Hydrogen sulfide
Hydroquinone
Hydroquinone monomethyl ether
2-Hydroxypropyl acrylate

Indene
Indium
Indium compounds
Iodine
Iodoform
Iron oxide
Iron pentacarbonyl
Iron salts, soluble
Isoamyl acetate
Isoamyl alcohol
Isobutyl acetate
Isobutyl alcohol
Isooctyl alcohol
Isophorone

Isophorone diisocyanate
Isophthalonitrile
Isopropyl acetate
Isopropyl alcohol
Isopropylamine
N-Isopropylaniline
Isopropyl ether
Isopropyl glycidyl ether

Kaolin
Ketene

Lead arsenate
Lead chromate
Lead
Lead, inorganics
Lime
Limestone
Lindane
Lithium hydride
LPG

Magnesia
Magnesium carbonate
Malathion
Maleic anhydride
Manganese compounds
Manganese cyclopentadienyl
  tricarbonyl
Manganese
Manganese tetroxide
MAPP
Marble
Mercury, alkyl compounds
Mercury, aryl compounds
Mercury, inorganic compounds
Mercury, metallic
Mesityl oxide
Methacrylic acid
Methacrylonitrile
Methane

Methomyl
Methoxychlor
Methyl acetate
Methyl acetylene
Methyl acrylate
Methylacrylonitrile
Methylal
Methyl alcohol
Methylamine
Methyl amyl alcohol
Methyl n-amyl ketone
N-Methyl aniline
Methyl bromide
Methyl carbamic acid,
  o-isopropoxyphenyl ester
Methyl chloride
Methyl 2-cyanoacrylate
Methylcyclohexane
Methylcyclohexanol
o-Methylcyclohexanone
Methylcyclopentadienyl
  manganese tricarbonyl
Methyl demeton
Methylene bisphenyl isocyanate
Methylene chloride
4,4'-Methylene bis(2-chloroaniline)
Methylene bis(4-
  cyclohexylisocyanate)
4,4-Methylenedianiline
Methyl ethyl ketone
Methyl ethyl ketone peroxide
Methyl formate
Methyl hydrazine
Methyl iodide
Methyl isoamyl ketone
Methyl isobutyl ketone
Methyl isocyanate
Methyl isopropyl ketone
Methyl mercaptan
Methyl methacrylate
Methyl parathion

Methyl propyl ketone
Methyl silicate
alpha-Methyl styrene
Metribuzin
Mevinphos®
Mica
Mineral oil
Mineral wool fiber
Molybdenum compounds
Monocrotophos
Morpholine

Naled
Naphtha
Naphthalene
alpha-Naphthylamine
beta-Naphthylamine
alpha-Naphthyl thiourea
Neon
Nickel carbonyl
Nickel metal
Nickel, soluble compounds
Nickel sulfide roasting
Nicotine
Nitapyrin
Nitric acid
Nitric oxide
p-Nitroaniline
Nitrobenzene
4-Nitrobiphenyl
p-Nitrochlorobenzene
Nitroethane
Nitrogen dioxide
Nitrogen trifluoride
Nitroglycerine
Nitromethane
Nitropropane
N-Nitrosodimethylamine
3-Nitrotoluene
Nonane

OCBM
Octachloronaphthalene
Octane
Osmium tetroxide
Oxalic acid
Oxygen difluoride
Ozone

Paper fiber
Paraffin wax
Paraquat
Parathion
PCBs
Pentaborane
Pentachloronaphthalene
Pentachlorophenol
Pentaerythritol
Pentane
Perchloroethylene
Perchloromethyl mercaptan
Perchloryl fluoride
Perlite
Phenol
Phenothiazine
p-Phenylene diamine
Phenyl glycidyl ether
Phenylhydrazine
Phenyl mercaptan
N-Phenyl-beta-naphthylamine
Phenylphosphine
Phorate
Phosgene
Phosphine
Phosphoric acid
Phosphorus, yellow or white
Phosphorus oxychloride
Phosphorus pentachloride
Phosphorus pentasulfide
Phosphorus trichloride
Phthalic anhydride
Picloram

Picric acid
Pindone
Piperazine dihydrochloride
Plaster of Paris
Platinum metal
Platinum, soluble salts
Portland cement
Potassium cyanide
Propane
Propane sultone
Propargyl alcohol
beta-Propiolactone
Propionic acid
Propoxur
n-Propyl acetate
Propyl alcohol
Propylene
Propylene dichloride
Propylene glycol dinitrate
Propylene glycol monomethyl ether
Propyleneimine
Propylene oxide
n-Propyl nitrate
Proteolytic enzymes
Pyrethrum
Pyridine

Quartz dust

Resorcinol
Rhodium metal
Rhodium compounds
Ronnel
Rosin core solder pyrolysis products
Rotenone, commercial
Rubber solvent, naphtha
Rutile

Selenium compounds
Sesone
Silane

Silica, amorphous
Silica gel
Silicon
Silicon carbide
Silver metal
Silver, soluble compounds
Soapstone
Sodium azide
Sodium bisulfite
Sodium fluoroacetate
Sodium metabisulfite
Stannic oxide
Stannous oxide
Starch
Stibine
Stoddard solvent
Strychnine
Styrene
Sucrose
Sulfotep
Sulfur dioxide
Sulfur hexafluoride
Sulfuric acid
Sulfur monochloride
Sulfur pentafluoride
Sulfur tetrafluoride
Sulfuryl fluoride
Sulprofos

2,4,5-T
Talc
Tantalum
Teflon® decomposition products
Tellurium
Tellurium compounds
Tellurium hexafluoride
Temephos
TEPP
Terphenyls
1,1,1,2-Tetrachloro-2,2-
    difluoroethane

1,1,2,2-Tetrachloro-1,2-
difluoroethane
Tetrachloronaphthalene
Tetraethyl lead
Tetrahydrofuran
Tetramethyl lead
Tetramethyl succinonitrile
Tetramethylthiuram disulfide
Tetranitromethane
Tetrasodium pyrophosphate
Tetryl
Thallium, soluble compounds
4,4'-Thiobis(6-tert-butyl-m-cresol)
Thioglycolic acid
Thiram
Tin metal
Tin compounds
Tin oxide
titanium dioxide
TNT
o-Tolidine
Toluene
Toluene diisocyanate
o-Toluidine
p-Toluidine
Toxaphene
Tremolite
Tributyl phosphate
Trichloroacetic acid
1,2,4-Trichlorobenzene
1,1,1-Trichloroethane
1,1,2-Trichloroethane
Trichloroethylene
Trichlorofluoromethane
Trichloronaphthalene
1,2,3-Trichloropropane
1,1,2-Trichloro-1,2,2-trifluoroethane
Tricresyl phosphate

Tridymite (silica)
Triethylamine
Trimellitic anhydride
Trimethylamine
Trimethyl benzene
Trimethyl phosphite
Triphenyl amine
Triphenyl phosphate
Tripoli (silica)
Tungsten compounds
Turpentine

Uranium compounds

Valeraldehyde
Vanadium pentoxide
Vegetable oils
Vinyl acetate
Vinyl bromide
Vinyl chloride
Vinyl cyclohexene dioxide
Vinylidene chloride
Vinyl toluene

Warfarin
Welding fumes
Wood dusts

Xylene
Xylidine

Yttrium

Zinc chloride
Zinc chromate
Zinc oxide
Zinc stearate
Zirconium compounds

APPENDIX 4
LETHAL DOSE EQUIVALENCIES

In the definitions for "toxic" and "highly toxic" health hazards found in Appendix A of the Standard, reference is made to LD50 and LC50 values. These definitions are given under conditions that often are different from those for which data are available in the literature. For purposes of identifying these types of hazards, such data can be translated into approximate values for the conditions used in the OSHA Standard definitions. Ultimately it may be advisable to rerun the tests under the same conditions as the Standard definitions.

The median lethal dose, expressed in milligrams per kilogram of body weight, is the dose that was found to be fatal to one half of the test animals under the stated conditions. The median lethal concentration in the air breathed by the animal, expressed in parts per million by volume, is the concentration that was found to be fatal to one half of the test animals.

SPECIES

For purposes of equivalencies between species, the various animals are divided into four groups, as in Table 8. For oral and inhalation toxicity, the chemical is to be tested on albino rats weighing between 200 and 300 g each. An exact equivalency between rats and some other species may not be possible, but some approximate translations are given here.

In the 1976 Edition of the NIOSH *Registry of toxic Effects of Chemical Substances,* a table of interspecies factors (page xviii) calculated from experimental data is given. Pertinent features of that table are summarized below and in Table 8.

Table 8. Groups of Animal Species Showing Equivalent Toxic Response

Group 1	Group 2	Group 3	Group 4
Frog	Mouse	Chicken	Cat
Gerbil	Rat	Duck	Cattle
Hamster	Squirrel	Guinea pig	Dog
	Mammal	Pigeon	Goat[a]
	(other)	Quail	Horse[a]
		Rabbit	Monkey
		Turkey	Pig
		Bird	Sheep[a]
		(other)	

[a]Domestic animals only.

For both oral and inhalation toxicity, LD50 and LC50 values are assumed to be the same for all members of Group 2 as for the rat. Values given for members of Group 1 should be multiplied by a factor of two to get the estimated value for the rat. And any values given for members of Groups 3 and 4 should be divided by two to get the estimated value for the rat.

For skin toxicity, for which the test animal is specified to be an albino rabbit weighing between 2 and 3 kg, LD50 values are assumed to be the same for all members of Groups 2 and 3 as for the rabbit. Values given for members of Group 1 should be multiplied by a factor of two to get the estimated value for rabbit. Values given for members of Group 4 should be divided by two to get the estimated value for the rabbit.

It must be remembered that all these equivalency translations are approximate only, with considerable margin for error. Whenever such a computation yields a value within a factor of about five of the limit of a defined range, the judgment of the hazard classification should be considered tentative. In such cases it is recommended that the appropriate test be run with the animal species and conditions specified in the Standard.

E. A. C. Crouch and R. Wilson have stated that the interspecies factor K seems to vary randomly from chemical to chemical with a lognormal distribution corresponding to an uncertainty of a factor of about five for comparison between species. (*Assessment and Management of Chemical Risks,* J. V. Rodricks and R. G. Tardiff, Eds., American Chemical Society, Washington, DC, 1984, p. 109). While this factor was evaluated for comparison of rats and mice with humans, and for carcinogens rather than for acute toxic response, it does give some indication of the uncertainty one might expect when translating other toxic data from one species to another.

INHALATION DOSE

For inhalation toxicity, the chemical is to be tested on albino rats weighing between 200 and 300 g each with continuous inhalation for 1 hr. However, for a large portion of the data reported in the literature, the inhalation period is much different from the 1 hr specified in the Standard.

In such cases, it would seem appropriate to use the product of concentration and exposure time to give the total dose administered. Henry's law says that the equilibrium solubility of a gas component in a liquid (the blood) is proportional to its concentration in the gas mixture, at a constant total pressure of the gas (the atmosphere). If the diffusion of the component through the lung tissue to the blood is a passive process (i.e., the cells in the lung tissue do not actively "push it through" to the blood), then the diffusion rate is also proportional to the difference in the concentrations of the component in the air and in the blood, from Fick's law. Combining these two factors, the total amount of the test substance that dissolves in the blood is expected to be approximately proportional to the product of the exposure time and the concentration in the air.

However, this will not always be a valid translation for at least two reasons. First, if the concentration of the material in the air is high enough, the diffusion rate and the equilibrium concentration in the blood may not be proportional to the concentrations as indicated above. Second, death from a short-time high-dose rate may occur by a different physiological mechanism than from a long-time low-dose rate.

However, in the absence of appropriate 1-hr data, the concentration that corresponds to the same total dose gives a reasonable approximation. For example, if the inhalation toxic dose for rats is reported to be LC50 = 65 ppm for a 4-hr exposure, it would seem to be a "highly toxic" substance. This would translate to 260 ppm (4 x 65) on a 1-hr exposure basis, though, which would indicate a "toxic" rather than a "highly toxic" substance.

INDEX

143

UPDATE

Hazard Communication And OSHA Requirements
By George G. Lowry and Robert C. Lowry
Respectively, Health and Safety Specialist and Attorney

This UPDATE and succeeding issues as required will be distributed free of charge with copies of the HANDBOOK OF HAZARD COMMUNICATION AND OSHA REQUIREMENTS. Subsequent issues will be produced, and included with the HANDBOOK, as required to keep the book current with changes in the Hazard Communication field as they occur.

UPDATE No. 1, December, 1985

Key Court Decision

On May 24, 1985, the United States Court of Appeals for the Third Circuit in Philadelphia issued its decision in *United Steelworkers of America v. Auchter.*

The Court first held that the HCS is a standard rather than a regulation, as those terms are used in the OSH Act. The effect of this is that the HCS explicitly preempts (to the extent that it is valid) state hazard disclosure laws with respect to disclosure to employees in the manufacturing sector.

The Court then ruled on three substantive issues. First, the Court found that OSHA's reliance on SIC Codes to define the standard's coverage "ignores the high level of exposure in specific job settings outside the manufacturing sector," and that OSHA failed to explain why coverage of workers outside the manufacturing sector would have seriously impeded the rulemaking process. It therefore ordered OSHA to reconsider application of the HCS to employees in nonmanufacturing sectors.

Next, the Court upheld OSHA's decision not to adopt the Registry of Toxic Effects of Chemical Substances (RTECS) compiled by NIOSH as part of the standard. OSHA may continue to rely instead on the hazard determination procedures contained in the HCS.

The court then turned its attention to trade secrets, and held that there is no legal justification for affording broader trade secret protection in the HCS than state law affords, and that the definition of trade secret adopted by OSHA must be revised so as not to protect chemical identity information which is readily discoverable through reverse engineering.

The Court also held that access to trade secrets may not be restricted to health professionals, although it seemed to indicate that the *number* of people having access may be restricted. The Court based its ruling on the assumption that employees who are not health professionals are no more likely to breach a confidentiality agreement than would the same number of health professionals.

Finally, the Court upheld the requirements that requests for secret information be in writing and that those making the requests must sign a confidentiality agreement.

The principal impact of the Auchter decision for employers in the manufacturing sector is on trade secret protection. OSHA has announced that it intends to publish a revised rule which conforms to the Court's ruling prior to November 25, 1985, when the HCS takes effect. As of the date of this writing (November 3, 1985), the revised rule has not yet been published.

OSHA has also announced that it plans to expand coverage of the HCS to include all employees, perhaps as early as Spring, 1987.

Public Right To Know

On October 10, 1985, the Third Circuit issued another decision on the issue of state law preemption. In an appeal of *New Jersey State Chamber of Commerce v. Hughey,* the Court reversed a portion of the district court's ruling that the HCS preempts community right-to-know laws applied to the manufacturing sector.

The appeals court ruled that state laws affecting disclosure of workplace hazards in the manufacturing sector may be "severable" from those affecting disclosure of environmental hazards. It therefore sent the case back to the district court to determine whether enforcement of the environmental hazard provision would interfere with accomplishing the purposes of the HCS.

148

OSHA's MSDS Form

OSHA is in the process of developing an MSDS form to replace their old Form 20. Use of the new form is expected to become mandatory for employers in the shipbuilding and ship repair industries, but its use would be optional for all others.

When properly filled out, the new form would meet the MSDS requirements of the HCS, as would any other form that contains the required information. The form included with THIS BOOK when originally published will also meet the requirements when properly filled out. It is designed such that backup technical data are to be entered on the second page of the form, making the information most needed by workers somewhat more easily accessible to them than in the case of the OSHA form.

At press time it was not known how soon the OSHA form might be available for public distribution, as it still must undergo one or more stages of review within the government. Unfortunately it was therefore not available for use by the initial compliance date of November 25, 1985, but it could be used later when MSDSs are revised.

OSHA stated that the purpose of this form is to assist chemical manufacturers and employers who do not want to devise their own MSDS forms. Since the OSHA form is becoming available so late in the process, it doesn't seem to serve the stated purpose as well as might be desired.

However, in view of the wide variety of MSDS formats that have appeared recently, there may well develop a clamor for some sort of standardization of MSDS forms in order to make information retrieval more convenient. If that should occur, then the form suggested by OSHA might become more widely used, even if it is not mandated.

Compliance Enforcement

In a set of guidelines issued by OSHA to its compliance officers, a number of specific instructions regarding compliance with the standard were issued. Some of the more important of these are mentioned here to help employers to prepare for an inspection experience that would be as uneventful as possible.

1. Evaluation shall be made of employer compliance with the written program requirements, use of labels, availability of MSDSs and appropriate training.
2. All available MSDSs shall be collected on every inspection.
3. *Violation citations shall be issued* when there is a complete lack of a written hazard communication program.
4. The adequacy of a hazard determination program shall be judged by accuracy and adequacy of information on labels and MSDSs.
5. The written hazard communication program shall be evaluated to determine whether it has been done in sufficient detail to ensure a comprehensive approach to hazard communication.
6. A "Representative number" of employees shall be interviewed to determine the general nature and effectiveness of the training program.

Determining Carcinogenicity

In Appendix C of the Compliance Guidelines mentioned above, some clarification is included regarding identification of carcinogens. A substance is to be included in the Hazard Communication program as a carcinogen if it meets any of the criteria listed below.

1. If a substance appears on the annual listing of the National Toxicology Program (NTP) as carcinogenic it is to be included.
2. If a substance is listed by the International Agency for Research on Cancer (IARC), it is to be included in the program if it is categorized by IARC as Groups I and II, but not if it is categorized as Group III.
3. Any substance which OSHA regulates as a carcinogen is to be included.

Compliance Checklist

In order to help assure employers that they will be found in compliance, the following checklist of the necessary features of a written program was developed using the compliance guidelines mentioned above:

* Hazard Evaluation
  - person(s) responsible
  - sources consulted
  - criteria used
  - review plan for new information
* Labels
  - person(s) responsible for in-plant labeling
  - person(s) responsible for shipping labels
  - description of label system
  - description of alternatives to labels, if used
  - review and update procedures
* MSDSs
  - person(s) obtaining and maintaining them
  - well-maintained and available
  - procedure when MSDS not received
  - procedure for updating
  - descriptions of alternatives to MSDSs in the workplace, if used
* Training
  - responsible person(s)
  - program format
  - program elements
  - initial training procedure
  - new-hazard training procedure
* List of Hazardous Chemicals
  - correspond with MSDSs
* Nonroutine Task Hazards
  - methods to inform employees
* Unlabeled Pipe Hazards
  - methods to inform employees
* On-Site Contractors
  - methods to inform them of hazards to which their employees may be exposed while working